THE
SOLAR PLANETS

V.A. FIRSOFF, MA, FRAS

David & Charles
Newton Abbot   London   Vancouver

Crane, Russak & Company, Inc.
New York

ISBN 0 7153 7352 8 (UK)
ISBN 0 8448 0964 0 (USA)
Library of Congress Catalog Card Number 76 5923

Set in 11 on 13pt Times
and printed in Great Britain
by Redwood Burn Limited Trowbridge
for David & Charles (Publishers) Limited
Brunel House Newton Abbot Devon

Published in the United States of America
by Crane, Russak & Company, Inc
347 Madison Avenue New York 10017

Published in Canada
by Douglas David & Charles Limited
1875 Welch Street North Vancouver BC

Contents

Acknowledgements

It is a pleasure to acknowledge the assistance I have received from several quarters in the preparation of this work. I feel especially indebted to the US National Aeronautics and Space Administration (NASA), and more particularly to Ames Research Center, Goddard Space Flight Center, Jet Propulsion Laboratory, and World Data Center A for Rockets and Satellites, and individually to Winifred Sawtell Cameron at Goddard Space Flight Center, for their most generous help in supplying the relevant information and illustrations. I also owe a debt of gratitude to the Branch of Astrogeologic Studies of the US Geological Survey, the Lunar and Planetary Unit of Lancaster University, *New Scientist*, the Novosti agency for the photographs of the surface of Venus by *Veneras 9* and *10*, the Librarians of the Royal Astronomical Society, Gordon H Taylor, Director of the Computing Section of the British Astronomical Association, and the US Information Service in London, who have all been variously helpful.

V A Firsoff

1

Between the old and the new

The coming of the space and computer age has inevitably caused many changes in the field of scientific research, and none has been more drastic than the transformation in astronomy. There is even a strong temptation to dismiss anything that dates from before, say, 1960 as obsolete; but this temptation should be resisted. The growth of scientific knowledge is a continuous process; there is still much wisdom to be found in the past, and the traditional observational techniques of astronomy are by no means dead.

We must accept, for instance, that the stars and galaxies remain as far away and as inaccessible as ever. Travel to other planetary systems, or even unmanned exploration of them, remains a pipe dream. Even in our own Solar System, flight to its outlying members takes a lot of time. The chief reason for this is the need to economise rocket fuel, which means giving the spacecraft a brief burst of speed and then leaving it, as it were, to its own devices, coasting free in the gravitational field. Close to the Sun this field is strong and steep, so that all orbital movements are fast, but their speed falls off sharply beyond the orbit of Mars.

The now-traditional and most economic way of getting from the orbit of our planet to that of another is by means of a Hohmann transfer orbit. A Hohmann transfer touches the two planetary orbits at its opposite ends, so that the spacecraft must go halfway round the Sun before reaching its destination.[1] On average, a Hohmann transfer to Venus takes 146 days and to Mars 259 days, which is lengthy but tolerable. But when we reach out to Pluto the corresponding period stretches to 16,650 days, which is quite unacceptable. If it were possible to make a bee-line for the target at parabolic velocity, the flight to Pluto could be cut down to 6,779 days, Venus 10½ days and Mars 24 days;[2] but this technique demands more power than we can at present afford.

Once we have the 'space shuttle' and a permanent space station in a parking orbit about the Earth, the ship will be able to take off from the station instead of from the ground. Since rising from the Earth's surface is the most expensive item in the 'velocity budget' of an interplanetary mission, this will open up new possibilities, including faster transfers.

In fact, we have already gone beyond Hohmann. The Hohmann flying time to Jupiter averages 997 days, but the *Pioneer 10* probe, launched from Cape Canaveral, Florida, on 3 March 1972, reached the giant planet in 725 days—a considerable saving. The probe is now on the way to the vicinity of Aldebaran, and if all goes well it may be there in 1,700,000 years. *Pioneer 11*, sent off to Jupiter on 5 April 1973, approached to within 26,600 miles of the planet's cloud decks on 2 December 1974 and, boosted by Jupiter's gravitational field, is now speeding on its way to Saturn, to arrive there about September 1979.[3]

As the Hohmann transfer to Saturn takes about six years this does not actually save time, but it does save rocket power. If the planets are favourably positioned relatively to one another, faster trajectories can be achieved by 'bouncing' the spacecraft off their successive gravitational fields, as planned in the now-abandoned American 'Grand Tours' of the Solar System.

Apart from the unmanned *Viking* landing on Mars and the double *Pioneer* flight to Venus of May–August 1978, the only surviving project is the *Mariner 11* Jupiter/Saturn mission. This will involve two spacecraft and is particularly intended for the study of Saturn and its satellites, including Saturn's largest moon, Titan. To be launched in 1977, the mission will pass Jupiter two years later and reach Saturn in 1981, thus cutting two years off the Hohmann time. The same technique has been used by the Venus/Mercury *Mariner 10*, of which more elsewhere. The trouble with the giant Outer Planets, however, is that they move slowly and the necessary configurations are very infrequent. Nor is there any way of reducing the message time. A radio signal takes 45 minutes to reach Jupiter—and 21 days to travel to Pluto.

So far, the only alien soil on to which Man has stepped has been that of the Moon. This has been done successfully and without loss of life on six occasions in the *Apollo* programme. But the latter has proved so expensive that further *Apollo* missions have been cancelled in favour of unmanned exploration and developing the space shuttle. The Moon, however, is only a relatively small companion world of the Earth, and although it may be said to have been brought almost within the scope of geographical exploration, our visits there have been brief and limited in extent.

For all that, our robot probes have already reached Mercury and Jupiter; automatic observing stations have been placed in orbit about Mars, and instrument packages have been landed on Venus and Mars. Most ingenious apparatus of this kind has been developed and tested, at least, on the Moon and Mars.

Obviously, no Earth-bound observer can compete with telescopic photography of a planet from only a few thousand or hundred miles above its surface, to say nothing of observations (human or automatic) made actually on the latter. Added to this is freedom from the optical obstruction of the Earth's atmosphere, which blocks out vast areas of the electro-magnetic spectrum. Mars alone seems suitable for manned exploration, and this is yet to come. Nevertheless, space flight has already revolutionised our knowledge of the Inner Planets, spectacularly widened our understanding of Mars and less so of the outer Jovian worlds, overthrown some long cherished beliefs and greatly restricted the scope of permissible conjecture.

Even our view of the Earth has acquired a new dimension through our being able to see it as a whole—a planet, and a smallish one at that—from orbital spacecraft and from the Moon.[4] The psychological, philosophical and scientific importance of this can hardly be over-estimated. Today surveying

from space, weather observation from space, satellite communication and even spying from space have become a workaday
part of our technological environment.

The idea of *Gaia*, developed by James Lovelock and Sidney
Epton, regards the Earth as a quasi-organism, the biosphere
and the atmosphere in particular being neatly balanced against
each other by a complex system of ecological interactions. This
notion certainly owes its birth to space flight. There are fears
that Man may upset this balance by his technological and even
agricultural activities, so that the poor *Gaia* may sicken or die,
the Earth becoming unfit for life. (Personally I think this to be
an exaggeration. Products of any process tend to oppose its
continuation—the so-called 'Le Chatelier principle'—and up-
sets in the global equilibrium will generally peter out after a
time. But this is another problem.)[5]

It is primarily this new knowledge with which *The Solar Planets*
is concerned. Our planets are designated 'Solar' not in order
to coin an unusual title, but to underline the fact that there are
other planetary systems, that such systems must indeed be a
commonplace in the commonwealth of the stars—little though
we may know about them as yet. We know even less about lone,
starless planets, quite a few of which must be cruising in deep
space. But we do know something about the Earth and the
Solar System; and knowledge, like charity, begins at home.

2

Planets, planetary systems and sub-systems

What is a planet?

'A coherent dark body orbiting a star' sounds a good definition, but this is not necessarily true. A 'black hole' might qualify, or a big chunk of rock, say 20 miles in diameter, pursuing an independent course round the Sun—there are quite a few such. We may well hesitate to accord it planetary status, although we would agree to call it a *planetoid*, or asteroid. There is also an alternative term—*minor planet*. What does this properly apply to? Vesta, with a diameter of 530km (320 miles) would qualify. On the other hand, a one-mile rock will probably be described as a *meteorite* or bolide. As there is no established convention for distinguishing between such bodies we may as well introduce one, at least provisionally.

Let us say that anything up to 5km (3 miles) in diameter is a meteorite, from 5–100km a planetoid or asteroid, and between 100–1,000km a minor planet. There are about a score of the latter between Mars and Jupiter, but the diameters of such small bodies are difficult to measure and are not accurately known.

The diameter of a small body can be determined if we know its distance, apparent brightness (*magnitude*) and *albedo*, which measures the proportion of incident light it reflects. If the incident light is taken as unity, then the reflected light is a fraction, and this is the albedo; eg, the albedo of the Moon is 0.07, which means that it reflects 7 per cent of the sunlight intercepted by it.

The apparent brightness and distance of a planetoid are known, but its albedo is somewhat elusive. There are two modern methods of getting to grips with it: polarimetric and radiometric. The polarisation of reflected light depends on the surface structure and varies with phase, so that it gives us information on its roughness, or smoothness, from which the albedo can be inferred. A dark body absorbs sunlight in the visual range and radiates in the infra-red (IR). When in thermal equilibrium it must radiate exactly the same amount of energy as it absorbs. Thus if we can measure its IR emission this should give us the absorbed fraction, which, subtracted from one, is the albedo.

The albedoes of minor planets vary a good deal. The 530km Vesta has an albedo of 0.20—it is as bright as sand. But Bamberga, with an albedo of 0.025, is blacker than soot. The average is about 0.15. Minor planets are dark bodies, and their diameters as determined by these methods are much larger than was previously assumed. There may also be minor planets or planetoids on the outskirts of the Solar System, where the feeble power of declining sunshine has failed to reveal them to our telescopes.

The lower size limit of 100km has some justification. G P Kuiper has calculated[6] that all bodies above this diameter will have experienced internal melting owing to the evolution of radioactive heat since the formation of the Solar System. This, of course, is only a very approximate estimate, involving various simplifying assumptions; but it does imply that such bodies will have assumed the basically spherical shape of hydrostatic equilibrium, like a raindrop, whereas the smaller ones may be irregularly shaped. Both these conclusions are in fair agreement with observation.

The upper limit of 1,000km, on the other hand, is purely arbitrary, although the largest known minor planet, Ceres, measures only 1,000km (610 miles) across. Then there is a big gap and the smallest planet, Mercury, has a diameter of 4,878km (3,010 miles). So in our planetary system, but this is probably the result of purely local conditions, and things may be different elsewhere.

But we still have to consider the other attribute of a planet—dark, or non-luminous.

At the present epoch no Solar Planet is obviously self-luminous. If the surface of Venus is really red-hot it ought to glow quite visibly, but so far there is no evidence that it does; and the ashen light on its dark side gives a line spectrum, characteristic of electric activity and not of thermal emission. Still, Venus does emit some light, and it will also look bright to a microwave eye (p 52). Jupiter and the other large Outer Planets radiate more heat than they receive from the Sun, so that they are luminous in the infra-red (IR) as well as in micro-waves. Even some of the Earth's internal heat seeps out to the surface, very gently, at the infinitesimal rate of 0.000072 gram-cals per cm² per minute,[7] which compares with the Solar heat at the Earth's orbit, or *Solar Constant*, of 2 gram-cals per cm² per minute.

There is, however, good evidence that at least the surfaces of Mercury, the Earth and the Moon were once blistering expanses of molten magma, glowing with a hellish glare. The giant planets might then have shone like stars. (This period of effulgent glory belongs to the infancy of the Solar System, and Venus seems unlikely to have lingered in that condition to the present day.) Supposing, however, we did break the light-barrier and set out to explore the universe, we could easily come across some planetary system at the corresponding stage of development. Would we deny planetary status to its small luminous bodies?

Luminosity is a matter not so much of *size* as of *mass*. Our Sun does not rank high in the hierarchy of stars. In fact it is depressingly (or reassuringly) average; but for this very reason its mass or $M\odot$, of 1.990×10^{30}kg, makes a handy standard of reference. The pride of our system, Jupiter, has a mass of roughly $0.001\ M\odot$, but we shall see that more massive planets exist. Their masses grade over smoothly into those of stars, for which the lower limit is conventionally set at $0.05\ M\odot$; less massive bodies cannot stay luminous for long.[8] We may be tempted to describe bodies of up to 0.002 $M \odot$, or twice the mass of Jupiter, as planets, and more massive ones as 'super-planets', but it is not very clear where the latter end and 'sub-stars' begin.

Satellites or planets?

Then, what about the Moon and other bodies with diameters between 1,000 and 6,000km, orbiting planets? The latter fact makes them satellites, and so bodies of a third gravitational order, which entails certain disabilities such as captured or tied-up rotation. This means that their orbital period about the planet (or primary) and axial period coincide, as though the satellite were tied to the planet with a string. No exception to this rule is known in the Solar System, but this is a matter of size. Tied-up rotation is the result of body-tides set up in the satellite by the nearby mass of the planet. In a more expansive system, where planets and their satellites are widely spaced, this need not happen. On the other hand, in a tight system where the planets are packed close to the central star (perhaps a star of small mass), the planets too may have tied-up rotations and always turn the same side to their sun. Mercury has narrowly escaped this fate.

Nor is there any good reason, other than lack of space, why a satellite should not have a sub-satellite of its own. Our Moon may be orbited by meteorites, but in a widespread system a super-planet could have a satellite of the mass of Neptune, orbited by another like our Earth; this in turn may have a smaller companion, and so on—if perhaps not *ad infinitum*.

The Moon does not differ all that much from, say, Mars, and its diameter of 3,476km is of substantially the same order of magnitude as the Earth's 12,756km (even though the latter exceeds the Moon 81.3 times in mass). They are comparable bodies. Moreover, the Moon moves about the Earth a good deal beyond the point where the gravitational pulls of the Earth and Sun draw level, so that its orbit is essentially Solar and only strongly perturbed by the Earth. Indeed, it seems that the Moon began its existence as an independent planet and was later captured by the Earth. In any case, it is quite usual to regard the Earth/Moon system as a double planet. This again is a likely development. There are double stars of comparable mass, and there may be double planets much more evenly matched than the Earth and the Moon.

Enough conjecture for the time being. Let us look at the Solar System as it is here and now.

The Solar family

The Sun has a diameter of 1,392,000km, 109.12 times that of the Earth, 328,900 of which would be required to make up mass $M\odot$, or one Sun. Yet the Sun is only a medium-sized 'dwarf' yellow star of spectral class G2V, radiating at an effective temperature of 5,800°K. A star of this class and mass has an estimated 'main sequence' sojourn of 13,000 million years, or 13 aeons and much longer, if the mass in its interior is mixed by convective currents, as now seems likely. If we put the Sun's age at 5 aeons, this leaves it with at least 8 aeons to go. This is important, for the main-sequence stars are characterised by a steady output of energy. This is derived from the processes of nuclear fusion in which four atoms of hydrogen are 'burned' to one atom of helium in the star's central core. The exhaustion of the central supply of hydrogen and leaving the main sequence is a more or less catastrophic event.[9] Our Sun's mass is too small for it to explode into a nova, but it may be thrown into pulsation and/or expand into a red giant, engulfing the inner-most planets. Even if the Earth were spared, life on it could hardly survive such a shock, although the giant Outer Planets might be comparatively unaffected.

The planets revolve around the Sun anti-clockwise in ellipti-cal orbits of small eccentricity. These orbits are comprised within a comparatively thin disc centred on the so-called 'Invariable Plane', which is determined chiefly by the great mass of Jupiter and is inclined at 1° 34′ 59″ to the plane of the Earth's orbit, or *ecliptic*. The planets are widely spaced, and their spacing is 'quantised' according to the approximate law of Bode and Titius, which can be expressed in the form: $a = 0.4 + 0.3 \times 2^n$.

In this formula a stands for the semi-major axis of the planet's orbit expressed in *astronomical units*, or AU, and n is the 'planet number'. AU is the mean distance of the Earth from the Sun, 149,600,000km (92,957,130 miles), known with great precision thanks to radar. For Mercury the second term on the right side of equality is omitted, and n starts with Venus, for which $n = 0$.

The actual mean Solar distances, diameters and densities of the planets are:[10]

TABLE I

PLANET	DISTANCE IN AU	DIAMETER IN KM	MEAN DENSITY IN g/cm^3
Mercury	0.387	4,878	5.44
Venus	0.723	12,100	5.25
Earth/Moon	1.00	12,756/3,476	5.52/3.34
Mars	1.524	6.790	3.94
Minor planets & planetoids	2.7–3.2	Various	2.0–6.0 (?)
Jupiter	5.203	142.200	1.33
Saturn	9.539	119.300	0.71
Uranus	19.182	47,100	1.71
Neptune	30.058	48,400	1.77
Pluto	39.364	5,900?	4.5?

Pluto is the odd man out. Its orbit, with an eccentricity of nearly 0.25, is inclined at over 17° to the plane of the ecliptic; it takes no notice of Bode and Titius; its mass is in doubt and its diameter and density are pure guesswork. The existence of still-undiscovered planets beyond Pluto is suspected.

According to Bode's formula there ought to have been a planet at about 2.85AU. Instead we find here a swarm of planetoids, some larger minor planets, as well as meteoritic debris; and 'debris' seems to be the word, for the bunching of planetoidal orbits suggests that they have originated in the break-up of a single larger planet, or perhaps a double planet brought into collision by the pull of Jupiter.

The French geologist S Meunier concludes from his researches that 'the meteorites present a complex of *stratigraphical relationships* and by correlating these one can reconstruct a *geological whole* which bears a strong resemblance to our globe'.[11] Two limestone meteorites have been reported, one of which fell in 1926 at Bleckenstad, southern Sweden, and is said to have contained fossils. This supposed planetary catastrophe can be dated from the exposure of meteorites to cosmic radiation: 520,000,000 years ago.[12]

Quite a few of the planetoids stray from the main belt and may turn up anywhere between Mercury and Saturn, and there may be others farther out.

Hypothetical planets apart, our table shows a tight bunch of four small *terrestrial* or Earth-like planets—Mercury, Venus, Earth and Mars. All these are solid, 'cannonball' worlds with relatively thin atmospheres (with some reservations in the case of Venus). Then, beyond the orbit of Mars, there is a gap of nearly 4AU before Jupiter introduces another foursome of wide-spaced giant planets attended by numerous moons, like miniature planetary systems. These giants have low mean densities, are surrounded by immense atmospheres of light gases, and seem to be heated from within. It is doubtful if Jupiter and especially Saturn, which is distinguished by a wide system of rings, have any solid surfaces at all; the higher densities of Uranus and Neptune make this possible, but by no means certain.

If it is taken into account that the mean density of a planet is affected by central compression, which increases with mass, there is a general tendency for planetary densities to decrease away from the Sun, though this trend is reversed beyond Saturn. A similar situation is clearly present among the large satellites of Jupiter.[13] All these regularities and peculiarities must be rooted in the conditions of birth of these systems. Pluto is usually reckoned among the terrestrial planets, but it is a somewhat mysterious body. Its density may be as high as 20; it may possibly belong to an older solar system, or else be an immigrant from interstellar space. It has been

suggested that Pluto may be an escaped satellite of Neptune—
but what could have perturbed the system of Neptune to cause
one of its members to break free? The dim and tiny planet
remains a puzzle that does not quite fit the specifications of its
fellows.

The Solar System is bathed in Solar weather in the form of
the 'wind' of protons and electrons, which waxes and wanes
with the Sun's spots and flares but weakens with distance.

In the beginning there was—chaos and confusion

All traditional accounts of the genesis of the world agree that
in the beginning there was chaos and confusion, and as far as
our understanding of the Solar System's origin is concerned
there still is. Many theories have been devised to account for
all the features of the Solar System, but none of them has won
general acceptance.

The first scientific attempts to explain how the planets arose
date from the eighteenth century and the philosophers Sweden-
borg (1734) and Kant (1755), and the mathematician Laplace
(1796) who, however, did not subject his idea to mathematical
analysis.[14] They envisaged a revolving cloud of gas—a nebula—
which spun faster and faster as it contracted, cast off rings at
its equator, and the rings then condensed into planets. Inspired
by Saturn and its rings, this theory had not been worked out
mathematically and ran into various difficulties, the main one
being that the Sun contains only 2 per cent of the angular
momentum of the Solar System, the remaining 98 per cent
being accounted for by the planets—which add up to about a
thousandth of the Sun's mass.

The nebular hypothesis fell out of favour towards the end of
the nineteenth century and was replaced by catastrophic
theories (Sedgwick, Chamberlin and Moulton, Jeans, Jeffreys
and Russell). These new theories involved either a close encounter or a grazing collision of the Sun and another star. Fred
Hoyle suggested[15] that the Sun had once been a member of a
binary system, a twin star. The Sun's twin had exploded into a

'supernova', the Sun held on to some of the ejected material, and this eventually condensed into the planets and satellites. The extremely high temperatures and velocities of expulsion in supernova explosions make this improbable.

In 1951 I suggested a more peaceable emission of matter by the Sun. This would become segregated under the combined action of pressure of radiation and centrifugal force according to atomic or molecular weight and thrown into a medley of intersecting orbits. Friction between the various streams would cause the ejecta to contract into a toroidal ring, from which the planets would be born. Emission of gaseous envelopes by stars is quite common, but these generally tend to dissipate without condensation. There are, however, some indications that the satellite systems of the giant planets may have arisen by a process not unsimilar to that envisaged by me. The trouble with all catastrophic theories is that they involve unlikely situations. The only feature to survive from Chamberlin and Moulton's theory is the idea of 'planetesimals': small condensations of nebular material that were later picked up by the larger ones and may still be represented by comets, meteorites and planetoids. But here again there are formidable objections; how could gases condense into bodies of such small mass? It is quite certain that the present compact, stony and iron-nickel meteorites cannot have originated in this way.

The theories most favoured today are those of *simultaneous origin* and its subsequent accretion, which are not mutually exclusive. In the first, the planets and the central star were formed from the same primeval nebula. In the second the Sun, originally single, captured material in passing through a nebula. This idea is particularly associated with the Soviet scientist O Y Schmidt. R A Lyttleton has shown that this could happen, provided that the speed of the star were sufficiently low relatively to the nebula (not more than 200m/sec).

The theories of simultaneous origin have been developed by C F von Weiszäcker in Germany, G P Kuiper in the USA[16] and Hannes Alfvén in Sweden,[17] the latter basing his ideas on the magnetic coupling between ionised gas and the star as a means of transferring momentum from the latter to the former. The ionisation energy is obtained from the fall of the gas towards the star under gravity. Kuiper and von Weiszäcker propose revolving cells, originating from the turbulent motions in the nebula, with viscous coupling and self-gravitational contraction causing these to 'wind up' into 'protoplanets', in Kuiper's view greatly exceeding in mass the present planets that have evolved from them. The excess mass is blown away by the luminous and corpuscular radiation of the central star when this begins to shine.

Fred Hoyle gathered the various threads from these hypotheses into a theory of his own, published in 1960.[18] He starts off with a contracting gas-and-dust cloud, or dark 'galactic globule', from which stars are known to form. From Alfvén he takes the idea of magnetic coupling, but without ionisation by fall. Both magnetisation and angular momentum are increased by contraction, so a nebula condensing into a star may be expected to spin fast and have a strong magnetic field. A cloud of plasma (ionised gas) surrounding a magnetic star will tend to revolve with it like a solid wheel. Thus the momentum is transferred from the central condensation (or the star-to-be) to the outer nebula (where the planets are born) by hydromagnetic coupling, which declines with the decreasing ionisation and magnetic field. Planetary condensations are determined by the boiling-point and chemical association of the various elements involved.[19]

The 'heavies' of relatively low abundance in the nebula will tend to form small dense bodies near the star (terrestrial planets), while hydrogen and other light elements will accumulate in giant planets at greater orbital distances. The rise in the mean densities beyond Saturn can be explained by the escape of hydrogen to space from the weakening grip of Solar gravitation. The satellite families of the giant planets would be formed by the same process, although this could not account for our Moon.

All this may be mathematically irreproachable but it deals with complex processes, and these must necessarily be oversimplified for any mathematical assessment. Sharp transitions are rare in nature, and observation is a much better test of reality.

Until recently we had no observational data on the formation of planets. There are, however—the T-Tauri stars—young stars, enveloped in gas and dust—on the point of emerging into full stardom and entering the main sequence. Some of them exhibit rapid changes of brightness; and one, RU Lupi, was chosen for special study by a group of four astronomers at Stockholm University, which has a southern station in Chile.

This study has revealed that the brightness fluctuations are not accompanied by spectral changes, such as would be expected if they were caused by flares or other violent activity on the surface of the star. They can best be explained as periodic obscuration by dark clouds—clouds of stellar dimensions but small mass (only about 0.001 of the Moon's), orbiting the star at planetary distances. We could thus have here the sort of planetesimals that could be expected to coalesce into larger planetary bodies.[20] All of this agrees with the ideas outlined above.

We also know a good deal about how stars are born. Being large and luminous they can be observed at various stages, so that their story can be pieced together. As stated above, the critical density which allows a large mass to condense under its own gravitation is much lower than for a small mass. Indeed, planets could not form straight from interstellar clouds at all, and stars of small mass are not much better off in this respect. What happens is that, owing to movements within the cloud or a collision between clouds, a critical density is reached in a certain area which contracts into a massive, very hot star, whose radiation ionises and heats up the surrounding gas. Thus a shell of hot gas expands into the cooler surrounding gas and sets up in it a compression wave, along which a whole rash of stars appears. This is the origin of expanding star clusters and associations. But smaller stars have the same effect within their own range, and set up further shells of compression within the compression wave, which allow still smaller masses to assemble under their own gravitation. The process is a continuous one, so that there is no good reason why quite small planetary masses could not arise in this way. Such planets would be animated by dispersive motions, inherited from the expanding gas, and would probably be loners unless captured by neighbouring stars.

However, let us consider a galactic globule with a central concentration of mass, as in Hoyle's, Kuiper's and other hypotheses.

It is already discoid and pre-condensed high above the level of the surrounding thin gas cloud. The central concentration is tightening upon itself and growing hotter and hotter; it begins to shine, at first purely thermally, by compression alone. Eventually the temperature of one million degrees C is reached, triggering off the proton-proton reaction and opening the door to true stardom.

Nuclear ignition may be sudden, but it is not a detonation. A completely new star will not be born all at once; to begin with its activity will affect only a small volume. For a long time the new star may remain quite invisible from the outer parts of the globule, as it will be swathed in dense opaque clouds—it is a *dark* globule. For all that, the newborn star will send out an expanding compression wave of mounting intensity into these surrounding clouds, acting in exactly the same way as when stars are formed—but, acting on clouds of small mass and high density, it will generate planets. Something of this kind seems to be happening around RU Lupi.

As the star brightens up, the gas and minor concentrations will be blown away, exactly as assumed by Hoyle, but the larger ones will survive, after being stripped of their outer atmospheric envelopes. Such is the origin of terrestrial planets. Farther out, where the globule is less dense, but also broader and less vulnerable to the pressure of radiation and corpuscular wind, the masses of the initial condensations will be larger from the start. They will have more time to grow, and will be able to preserve most of their primitive atmospheres, giving rise to Jovian planets. These in turn will develop into temporary sub-stars and repeat the process within their narrower ambits, generating satellite families.

The fundamental point is that stars and planets would be formed by exactly the same process. The differences are quantitative, not qualitative; they are a matter of the available mass, density and timing. Massive stars would tend to stay alone or produce stellar companions rather than small planetary ones, but the common run of stars would be only up to planets.

How many planetary systems?

Two or three years ago Shiv S Kumar kindly sent me a preprint of his article on planetary systems, due to be included in *The Emerging Universe*, published by the University Press of Virginia. In this he concludes that 'the total number of such systems is unlikely to be more than 10^6 even though the number of stars in the Galaxy is 10^{12} or more'.[21] He even hints, a little vaguely, that there might be only one planetary system—our own Solar System—in the whole of the Milky Way spiral.

This would have delighted the Fathers of the Holy Inquisition had they been alive today, but in astronomical circles his view is somewhat isolated. At the Byurakan (USSR) Conference in September 1971, attended by many eminent scientists from all over the world, it was mooted that the Galaxy may contain some 50,000 million planets, sustaining between 100,000–1 million technological civilisations.[22] Even this estimate may fall short of the mark. It is, nevertheless, of some interest to consider how Kumar has arrived at his conclusion.

First, he defines a planetary system as one whose most massive planet holds not more than 0.01 of the mass of the central star. This, he says, is meant 'to distinguish a planetary system from a double or a multiple star system'. Such a limitation, however, is wholly arbitrary, for it implies (without proof) that there can be no planets in double or multiple star systems. Comments on the orbital stability of minor members of such systems can only carry weight within a rigidly, and again arbitrarily, imposed framework. The Earth's orbit might well become unstable if the mass of Jupiter were doubled. But it is enough to remove this double-sized Jupiter to the distance of Saturn to parry the threat.

Kumar also observes, soundly enough, that most of the invisible dark companions of the neighbouring stars are too massive to be regarded as ordinary planets. Yet this does not entitle us to conclude that the same stars cannot have other smaller invisible companions. Kumar simply put such systems among 'double stars', and thus disqualifies them by definition. His pronouncement that 'the processes of star formation are different from planet formation' is at best questionable.

Jupiter has fourteen known satellites, including Ganymede, which exceeds Mercury in size if not in mass, and Callisto, which is not far behind. There is no compelling reason to suppose that the same processes as have produced Jupiter and its satellites could not have formed a body of twice or even ten times its mass. The latter might be a 'degenerate', or super-dense, 'black dwarf', a couple of hundred miles in diameter. (In fact, Jupiter's mass is supposed to be close to the boundary value where degeneracy sets in—a condition derived from equations based on various simplifications, which are always suspect.) Nevertheless, degenerate or not, this need not prevent its having a retinue of satellites, some of which could exceed the Earth in mass. Saying that such bodies are not planets is empty pedantry.

The central star orbited by this dark companion could have an independent group of planets of its own. We would thus have a double planetary system. The satellite families of the Outer Planets are, in fact, such systems in miniature, so that the Solar System could be described as multiple. All that is needed to make the situation unmistakable is to expand the scale and increase the masses of the Jovian planets so as to make them self-luminous stars.

V G Fessenkov contends[23] that there could be no life on the planets of double and multiple stars, for, says he, their orbits are 'inevitably marked out by an extremely complicated shape. Thus isolated stars alone may have inhabited planets in their neighbourhood'. Since he further follows Kuiper in assuming that 80 per cent of all stars are double or multiple, the number of planetary systems capable of sustaining life must be correspondingly limited. This view may not be as extreme as Kumar's, but it has a similar pedigree.

Figures-of-eight and more complicated orbits are *possible* in close double-star systems, but they are not *inevitable*, nor are they necessarily deadly. It is all a question of mass and spacing. At the distance of Saturn our allowance of Solar heat and light is reduced to 0.01. Thus a second Sun placed there would have hardly any effect on our climate. A blue star of $2.5M\odot$ could not be more than fifty times as luminous. Radiating from that distance it would supply about a half of the Solar Constant, largely in the ultra-violet, which would intensify our ionosphere and ozonosphere (see p 38), but need not be catastrophic to life on Earth. At the distance of Pluto, where the Sun subtends an angle of $50''$ and so is little more than a very bright star, the energy flux of this blue star would only be 0.03 Solar Constants.

Some double stars are so close together that they almost touch. Others are much farther apart than Pluto and the Sun, and take thousands of years to complete one revolution. In the system of Castor two close binaries revolve around each other in 300 years. Such close binaries could be orbited by a planet as though they were a single mass. γ Andromedæ is a most colourful assembly. A blue star of $2.4M\odot$ is coupled to a green one of $2.7M\odot$ in a 56-year period, and both of them orbit a yellow giant of $7.5M\odot$ at 800AU in 600 years.[24] What minor members this system may contain is anybody's guess.

The time has come to introduce these invisible dark companions.

The Moon does not just revolve about the Earth, nor the Earth about the Sun; in both cases the two masses revolve about their common centre of gravity. The orbits they describe, however, are inversely proportional in size to the ratio of their masses. Thus the Earth has no observable effect on the Sun, but the Moon makes the Earth swing about a point near its perimeter in a way that would be readily measurable from another planet. When the masses are large and more evenly matched, the resulting positional wobble is detectable even at stellar distances. This is how the existence of invisible companions has come to light.

The first of them was discovered in 1936 by D Reuyl near the star Ross 614. It has a period of 15 years and a mass of $0.04M\odot$ (more than 40 times that of Jupiter). Although invisible it is clearly stellar, possibly a black dwarf.

The chances are heavily weighted against the detection of a positional wobble due to invisible companions. In the first place, the star must be sufficiently close for the wobble to be measurable. In the second, the companion must be sufficiently massive in relation to it to produce an appreciable fluctuation of position. The movement of the Sun due to the attraction of Jupiter, which measures $0.00097M\odot$, is at best at the limits of observability even with the nearest stars. In the third, the star itself has usually some peculiarity, such as a very large proper motion among other stars, which attracts regular measurements of its position.

As a result the list of known invisible companions is a collection of oddities, favouring super-planets and sub-stars between 0.002 and $0.05M\odot$ on the one hand, and small dwarf stars on the other. Thus we have:[25]

The UV Ceti system of two sub-stars of 0.044 and $0.035M\odot$ and an orbital period of 200 years:

Cinc 1244	having a dark companion of	$0.032M\odot$
o² Eridani	,,	0.029
Lalande 21185	,,	0.01 (approx)
70 Ophiuci	,,	0.01
61 Cygni B	,,	0.008
Proxima Centauri	,,	0.0018 (?)

Only the last qualifies as a planet according to our definition (p 14), and it is no accident that Proxima is both the nearest of all stars and has a mass of barely $0.1M\odot$. This is, however, a somewhat doubtful case. The only true planetary system known is that of Barnard's Star.[26]

Here again we have a red dwarf of small mass ($0.15M\odot$), with a large proper motion, six light-years away. Some latest data suggest that a complicated disturbance of its motion is best explained by the presence of three large planets, between Jupiter and Neptune in mass, one of which has an orbit inclined at some 40° to the other two. (This goes to show that planetary systems need not be co-planar. Our Pluto has an inclination of 17°, and some planetoids have even steeper orbits.) According to O Jensen and T Ulrych of the University of British Columbia, a rigorous analysis of the perturbations of Barnard's Star implies a system of five planets, all of them in the Jovian class, with periods of 2.4, 2.9, 3.8, 11 and 26 years.[27]

Thus our knowledge of other planetary systems remains small and lopsided, but the fact that so many of our nearest stellar neighbours have planetary and super-planetary companions is significant. Both in the Solar System and among the stars in general, small masses are far more numerous than large ones, and it seems a fair guess that this is universal. In other words, there must be planets galore.

As mentioned above (p 18), nearly the whole of the angular momentum of the Solar System is vested in its planets, the huge mass of the Sun accounting for barely 2 per cent. The Sun is also a slow spinner, turning once round in $25\frac{1}{2}$ days. This seems to be a common feature of yellow, orange and red dwarf stars —and these are the most numerous of all stars. Slow spinning has been interpreted by W H McCrea, S S Huang and Otto Struve as due to the transfer of angular momentum from the star to the planets, which could mean that all such stars have planetary companions. True, it has been contended by Evry Schatzman and V G Fessenkov that the momentum may have been carried away by the corpuscular wind.[28] Still, our Sun is a slow spinner, and it has planets.

The mass of our Galaxy is $1.1 \times 10^{11} M\odot$, so that it must contain a comparable number of stars. If only 1 per cent of these have planetary systems there will be a thousand million of them, with a few planets in each. To how many 'technological civilisations' this might correspond it is impossible to guess; but I am not too sure that even in the Solar System ours is the only one.[29]

3

The third Solar Planet

The Earth–Moon system will be a brave sight when approached from interplanetary space: first a double blue-and-yellow star, then drawing apart and turning into discs, that of the Earth some three-and-a-half times wider and much more brilliant than that of the Moon, for the Earth reflects 35 per cent and the Moon only 7 per cent of the Sun's light. We have yet to see it like that, but we know what our Earth looks like from the Moon: a large, dark-blue marble, streaked with white swirls of cloud, and now and again some land mass peeping out uncertainly, grey-blue or Mars-red.

It is doubly beautiful to us, for it is our home; and the still more magnificent Jupiter or Saturn with its shining rings are alien worlds and do not touch our hearts. Yet even on objective reckoning the Earth is the chief of the terrestrial clan of planets; but for all that it is one of many planets, known and unknown, and is best understood in relation to them.

A geologist or a geophysicist thinks of the terrestrial globe in structural and physical terms, but what interests us surface-dwellers most is its exterior. The Earth is an ecological whole, and so more than the sum of its parts, and many things go into its making.

Under the Earth's skin

Composition is important; so far as the solid ball itself is concerned the terrestrial planets do not appear to differ very much in this respect, always with due reservations in the case of Pluto.

The mean density of the Earth works out at 5.52 times that of water, but its surface rocks average only about 2.7. There is some varied increase in density with depth, but at 6.4km or so below the oceans and 20–50km under the continents it suddenly jumps up to 3.32, which reveals itself by the behaviour of earthquake, or seismic, waves. This is *Mohorovičić's discontinuity*, named after its Yugoslav discoverer. Being a bit of a mouthful, it is usually referred to as the 'Moho'. Our uppermost rocks, typified by granite and the products of its decay, are given the descriptive name of *sial* from their main constituents *si*licon and *al*uminium. There is not a great deal of sial, and if evenly spread all over the Earth's surface it would make a layer some 10km thick; but it is bunched up under the land masses and is virtually absent from the ocean floors.[30]

Below the Moho the rocks are *sima*, in which *si*licon and *ma*gnesium predominate. They are darker and heavier, rather like basalt, spouted by some volcanoes and poured out as lava in fissure eruptions.

As we dig into the bowels of the Earth, the temperature rises steadily by some 2.5°C per 100 metres. Over 30km this makes 750°C. At such temperatures basalts begin to melt. Fusion is prevented by the pressure of the rocks overlying the Moho, but the material beneath it is semi-plastic; it acts like a kind of rubber cushion, which subsides under a heavy overlay and redresses itself when the burden is lightened. This is called 'isostasy', and is responsible for the variable depth of the Moho itself and the corresponding differences in the altitude of the surface.

Sial is not only lighter than sima; it also has a higher melting point, so that it tends to float on the latter rather like slag on molten iron. Thus sial has been steadily pushed up towards the surface. The basement rocks are everywhere igneous, which shows that at one time the surface must have been at or near the melting-point of silicates; but even today the temperature continues to rise with depth in the so-called 'mantle' below the Moho, and this point is certainly passed.

Only the enormous pressures prevent liquefaction, but there

are slow currents in the mantle, forming convection cells, which may shift the position of the continents over geological ages; and sialic components continue to rise towards the surface. This is *geological fractionation*, or the separation of materials according to composition, specific gravity and melting-point. Water and other volatile constituents likewise escape from the depths, mainly through volcanic vents.

As a result of such processes we have land and sea. On average the land stands 900 metres above the sea, reaching 9,712 metres at Mt Everest in the Himalayas (which, incidentally, are still growing). The mean depth of the sea is about 4km, but in oceanic trenches this sinks to 11km. Terrestrial mountains are mainly of the folded, chain or arcuate type, sculptured by ice and water and described as 'alpine'. They are believed to have been produced by the squeezing-out of the relatively light sediments accumulated in the deep troughs at the edges of ancient land masses. This process occurred during the collision of mobile 'tectonic plates', which provide more or less enduring bases for the continents.

But there are also elevated and depressed regions: broad linear valleys (such as the Great East African Rift Valley), and scarp mountains (as in the western USA), both produced by up-and-down movements along crustal fractures, or faults. Another type of mountain formation seems to have been common in the early periods of the Earth's history: subsidence within a sub-circular fracture with volcanic activity around the edge, resulting in a vast, mountain-ringed depression. In 1963 A R Crawford[31] discovered remnants of such structures, 90 and possibly 170km in diameter, in an ancient (pre-Cambrian) complex in South Australia; in 1965 W E Elston[32] studied the similar Mogollon Plateau in New Mexico. This is 145km wide and much better preserved. But all of them are exceeded by volcanic rings, dated at between one and three aeons, which J B Kloosterman[33] brought to light in 1973 in the obscure regions of northern Brazil, Venezuela and Guyana. These measure 500 by 900km, 300 by 350km, and 600km in diameter respectively; and though atypical of the present conditions on

Earth they bear a strong resemblance to some prominent structures on the Moon, Mercury and Mars.

However, in the mantle below the Moho the temperature and density continue to rise towards the centre of the globe; the density, it is thought, chiefly through structural changes in crystalline habit (although one is inclined to suspect an increasing proportion of nickel-iron). Then, at 2,900km below the surface, we encounter another sharp discontinuity. The density leaps from 5.5 to 10.0, and the material transmits seismic waves like a liquid. We have reached the Earth's core, believed to consist mainly of iron and nickel (by analogy with the iron-nickel meteorites); and referred to as *nife* from the chemical symbols for nickel (Ni) and iron (Fe). The seismic behaviour changes once more some 1,300km from the centre, with a jump in density from 12.3 to 13.3. This inner core responds to earthquake waves like a rigid solid, but it may be strongly compressed gas. The rising density is attributed to compression alone and reaches 13.6 in the middle of the Earth,[34] where the temperature is (very uncertainly) estimated at $14,000°K^2$.

It would thus be stellar.

We have seen (p 13) that very little of this internal heat leaks out to the surface; the reason for this is that rocks are very poor thermal conductors. Only locally does magma (molten rock) reach daylight along crustal weaknesses to form volcanoes; sheet outflows occur mainly on ocean beds along the active ridges, but they are well known in Iceland in our times and elsewhere in the past. Both internal compression and internal heat are functions of mass; and internal heat may determine the surface climate on more massive planets (see Chapter 8).

As indicated (p 12) the Earth's internal heat is due to the radioactive fission of such elements as thorium, uranium and potassium-40. It also seems that the rate at which it is generated is slightly in excess of its rate of escape at the surface, so that periodically (about once every 250 million years) the interior of the Earth overheats. This leads to greatly increased volcanic activity and mobility of the surface elements, which marks the peak period of mountain building. There are climatic changes, due to the exhalation of immense amounts of gas from the volcanoes. It is possible that the total mass of the Earth's atmosphere is temporarily increased, but an increase in humidity and the content of carbon dioxide can certainly be expected.

The situation is not clearly understood. The disturbance continues for some millions of years, and is often followed by an ice age.[35] Whether this is merely local (due to a change in the position of the poles and continental drift) or reflects a more general deterioration of the climate, is not known.

The records of the rocks bear witness to many past ice ages involving such unlikely places as India, Brazil and South Africa. Mountain-building volcanic periods alternate with long ages of relative quiescence and intensive denudation (literally 'laying bare'), when mountains are worn down, sediments accumulate and deserts begin to spread.[36]

Gravity and atmosphere

The importance of the Earth's mass has been clearly underlined in the foregoing section. One of its direct manifestations is gravity, or the force of attraction it exerts on other masses, which we experience as weight. If this force were weak there could be no effective geological fractionation, and many familiar geological processes would be inhibited or profoundly modified. Gravity is responsible for internal compression. But as the latter *increases* towards the centre of the globe, gravity *decreases*, to become zero when the centre is reached. Thus a planetary structure with a hollow centre is possible.[37] It would have to be filled with a very hot gas, generating sufficient pressure, kinetically (ie by molecular motion) or by radiation, to sustain the weight of the enclosing shell. But this is all a matter of degree and a small cool body, which had been very hot to begin with, might assume the form of a hollow shell.

Gravity also declines as we move away from the Earth. Yet what we are primarily concerned with is *surface* gravity, which

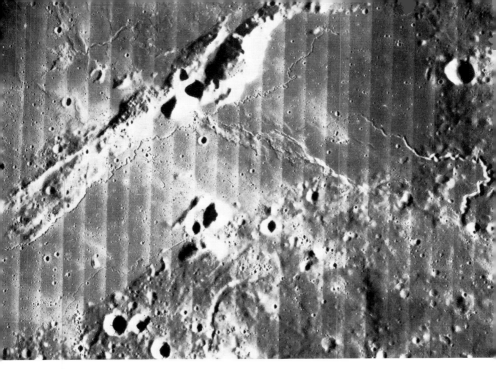

Plate 1 Orbiter photograph shows sinuous rilles and tholoidal peaks and ridges in the east of the Ocean of Storms on the Moon. Note the long thin meandering channel; can this really be explained away as a collapsed lava tube? (see p. 81) *(NASA)*

Plate 2 On the lunar surface: telephoto shot by the *Apollo 15* crew of the Silver Spur, Hadley Delta area, Lunar Apennines. Rock stratification clearly visible *(NASA)*

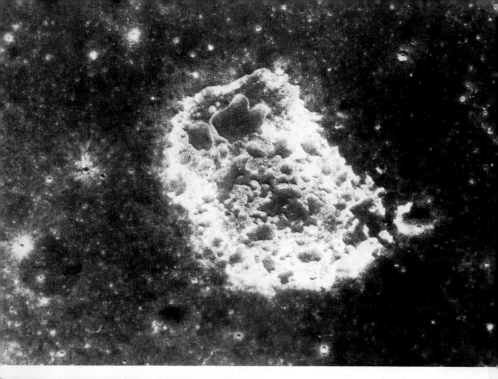

Plate 3 (above) Volcanic activity on the Moon. Blister domes and bright incrustation, photographed by *Apollo 8 (USIS, London)*

Plate 4 (left) The iron planet: an 18-picture mosaic of Mercury, taken by *Mariner 10* on 29 March 1974. Dominant feature is the sunlit half of the Caloris Basin, at centre left *(Jet Propulsion Laboratory)*

is measured in terms of the acceleration imparted to a freely falling body in the absence of air resistance. Its sea-level value on Earth, or g, is 980cm per square second, which means that the velocity of a body so falling will increase by 980cm/sec every second. Surface gravity is directly proportional to the planet's mass and inversely proportional to the square of its radius. Although the mass of Saturn is 95 times as large as the Earth's, its radius is 9.3 times larger as well, so Saturn's surface gravity is only some 16 per cent higher. On the Moon it is $\frac{1}{6}g$, which enabled the heavily-clad Apollo astronauts to do their 'kangaroo hop'; on Jupiter, where surface gravity is nearly 2.6g, they would not be so frisky.

Atmosphere, too, has weight. Barometric pressure is proportional to gravity, which thus determines the boiling-points of water and other liquids. It affects the structure of the atmosphere, the strength of the winds and the height of the clouds.

The very existence and composition of the atmosphere depends on the mass of the planet—not through gravity as such, but through the related quantity of *escape velocity*. This is the velocity a body must develop permanently to leave the planet in unobstructed flight. The velocity of escape from the Earth's surface is 11.18km per second. Yet, although Saturn's surface gravity is only a little over our g, the corresponding escape velocity is 36.26km per second—its great mass tells.

Molecules in a gas move at all sorts of velocities, colliding and rebounding, but statistically these real velocities cluster round the *mean-square-root velocity*, the square of which is directly proportional to the absolute temperature of the gas and inversely to its particle (molecular) mass. Suppose the gas were exposed directly to the vacuum of space in the gravitational field of the planet. A few molecules would exceed the velocity of escape in the right direction and sail away for good and all. The higher the mean-square-root velocity of the gas, the more often this will happen, so that cold heavy gases will tend to linger, and light hot ones stream off to space rather rapidly.

But the escape velocity depends on the mass of the planet.

Thus bodies of small mass, unless very cold, will not be able to retain light gases for long. This is why the Moon is more or less airless, and even the Earth's mass is too small to retain hydrogen, the most abundant gas in the universe and in the atmospheres of the giant planets.

The first systematic investigation of the situation was carried out by Sir James Jeans in the 1920s,[38] but, as is often the case, he oversimplified the problem.

First of all, a molecule to be able to escape must be physically present at the escape level (which water molecules will generally not be, because water vapour is substantially frozen out of the atmosphere before this level is reached). Then, molecular evaporation to space is, like ordinary evaporation, an effective process of refrigeration. The gas loses its most energetic molecules, so that its energy content (heat) and its temperature steadily diminish until further escape will effectively cease.[39] Interplanetary space contains a little gas, so that the density of the escape level can never fall below that of the interplanetary gas.

Furthermore, the gas at the escape level will be more or less thoroughly *ionised*. In ionisation one or more electrons are split off the atom, so that this results in a gas of free electrons— and the particle mass of an electron is 1,840 times smaller than that of a hydrogen atom. Being so light, the electrons will escape to space almost instantly, leaving behind a positive electric charge. This charge will eventually become sufficiently strong to hold back the electrons by electrostatic attraction, but by the same token it must induce a negative charge in the layer of gas or in the ground below it. This holds back the gas at the escape level electrostatically, in addition to gravity.[40]

And so the process of molecular evaporation to space contains its own brakes. On the other hand there is the Solar Wind of electrons and protons, streaming by at thousands of kilometres per second, which represents a serious threat to tenuous atmospheres in the absence of a strong magnetic field. But this wind, too, has to contend with electric fields. The situation is very complicated; the rates of escape of atmospheric gases have been greatly overestimated in the past—and still are.

For all that, the Earth has an atmosphere which exerts at sea-level an average pressure corresponding to the weight of a layer of mercury 760mm thick, which is called one 'atmosphere'. The convention of expressing atmospheric pressures in millimetres of mercury (mmHg), also known as *torr*, has originated in the use of a mercury column in old-fashioned barometers. The modern unit is the millibar (mb); 760mmHg = 1,013.25 mb.

The percentage composition of the Earth's atmosphere by volume is as follows: nitrogen (N_2) 78.09, oxygen (O_2) 20.95, argon (A) 0.93, carbon dioxide (CO_2) 0.03, helium (He) 5.2 × 10^{-4}. The proportion of carbon dioxide varies within narrow limits, as it is one of the industrial and volcanic pollutants, and is used up by green vegetation in photosynthesis. Also variable is the proportion of water vapour, which is confined to the lower atmosphere by the 'cold trap'—the low temperature at the tropopause (*see below*), where it is almost completely frozen out. Ozone (O_3), on the other hand, is found mainly in the upper atmosphere, again in variable proportions, but its total amount is barely one-millionth of a percent. Yet it provides a most effective shield against the harmful short ultra-violet (UV) radiation.

For a given composition, atmospheric density is determined by pressure and temperature alone. It is therefore convenient to refer it to *standard conditions of temperature and pressure* (STP), set at 0°C and one atmosphere. If the whole of the Earth's atmosphere were at STP it would form a layer about 9km (5½ miles) deep; this is called the *equivalent atmosphere*, or *air mass*, a concept that is useful for comparisons with other worlds, atmospheric absorption, refraction, etc.

Structure of the atmosphere

The atmosphere is not just so much air. It has a structure. The lowermost part or *troposphere* extends up to the tropopause, at

8–18km. The height of the tropopause depends on the ground temperature, and varies with seasons and geographical latitude, being greatest at the Equator and smallest at the poles. The troposphere is also described as the convective atmosphere, for it is characterised by vertical and horizontal air flow (convection), with cloud formation, precipitation, etc; it is the seat of weather. In the troposphere the air temperature decreases steadily with height, usually by about 6.5°C per km. This is the so-called *dry adiabatic lapse rate*—once again an abstraction.[41]

At the tropopause the temperature drops to 219°K (−54°C) —the 'cold trap'—in the latitude of Britain; it is somewhat higher near the poles and lower above the Equator. This temperature stays constant throughout the *stratosphere*, or isothermal (uniform temperature) atmosphere, which extends up to 30km. This region is almost devoid of clouds and vertical air currents. Between 30–80km lies the *mesosphere* or ozonosphere, characterised by the presence of ozone. This triatomic form of oxygen is formed from ordinary diatomic oxygen by the action of UV radiations, which it greedily absorbs and becomes heated as a result. The temperature at 60km attains 370°K (or what would be the boiling point of water at ground level). The temperatures remain high above 80km, but the air densities are so low there that it is practically a commercial vacuum. Then comes the *ionosphere*. At 100, 200 and 300–400km there are variable ionised layers, which respond to Solar weather and reflect radio waves.

The molecular spray of the *exosphere* spreads even further out, and at the height of 1,000km there is still enough gas to produce the rare daylight aurorae, though the usual displays of polar lights occur at about a tenth of this altitude. Finally, the Van Allen belts of solar particles (mainly protons), trapped in the Earth's magnetic field, ring the Equator at about 2,000 and 30,000km.

Such is the gas halo of the Earth, which may be taken to characterise a similarly constituted planet of comparable mass $(5.976 \times 10^{24}\text{kg})$, receiving a comparable amount of energy from the central star. But there is always room for differences, and the atmospheres of the other terrestrial planets in our system have not developed on quite the same lines.

Anyway, the Earth's atmosphere shelters a body of water, or *hydrosphere*, which in the form of the seas accounts for an area of 361.3 million square km, as against the 148.8 million square km occupied by land.

Climate

The atmosphere is a very important item in the complex entity of planetary climate.

Except for the Outer Planets, the temperature of a planet must necessarily be governed by its distance from the Sun. The energy of sunlight obeys the inverse square law: at half AU it will be four times our Earth's Solar Constant, and a ninth of it at 3AU. This, however, measures only the energy flux at the orbit in empty space. What really counts is the energy absorbed by the planet; and this depends on the *albedo*, the percentage of radiation which is reflected.

The Earth's albedo is estimated at 0.35, that of Venus 0.75. The two planets reflect 35 and 75 per cent of the Solar energy respectively. Although the distance of Venus from the Sun is only 0.72AU, at which the unobstructed Solar flux is 1.9 times that of ours, in actual fact Venus retains 15 per cent *less* of the Sun's heat than the Earth—and that at the cloud level, where the reflection occurs.

From the albedoes the theoretical 'greysphere' temperatures of radiative equilibrium can be readily obtained: 249.2°K for the Earth and 228.8°K for Venus. But they represent only the equilibrium temperatures at which the two planets re-radiate the energy they receive from the Sun. To be at thermal equilibrium, the two sides of the account must balance, or else the temperature would be either rising or falling.

The actual surface temperature depends on the complicated traffic between it and the atmosphere. To describe the situation, I will requote from my *Life Beyond the Earth* Harry Wexler's amended account of the situation, taken from *Climatic Change* (p 74):[42]

> Of the 100 units of solar radiation (of wavelengths 0.2μ to 3μ) impinging on the atmosphere, 35 units (the Earth's albedo) are reflected to space by air, clouds, and Earth, and therefore do not contribute to the energy of the atmosphere; 14 units are absorbed by clouds, dust particles, and various gases in the atmosphere (principally water vapour and ozone), leaving 51 units to arrive at the Earth's surface, 34 units as direct solar radiation and indirect sky radiation that results from the scattering of direct solar rays by air molecules and other small particles in the atmosphere, and 17 units as indirect solar radiation transmitted and scattered by the clouds.
>
> The Earth, radiating as a black body at its observed average surface temperature of 287°K, sends up 113 units of long-wavelength (4μ to 1μ) radiation. Because water vapour strongly absorbs radiation in most of these wavelengths, the atmosphere is very nearly opaque to the terrestrial radiation. Only 17 units escape directly to space unhindered by the atmosphere; the atmosphere, absorbing 96 units, returns 90 units to Earth, thus leaving only 23 units to comprise the 'effective outgoing radiation' as it would be measured by a radiation instrument located at the Earth's surface. The atmosphere gains 6 units of the terrestrial radiation and emits 48 units to space. Totalling the various incoming and outgoing radiations, there is an overall balance at the top of the atmosphere, a net loss of 28 units in the atmosphere, and a net gain of 28 units at the Earth's surface. The net energy gain at the surface is mostly utilised in evaporating water, which rises as vapour and is condensed into clouds and precipitation, releasing the heat of condensation, and thus making good the deficit of energy in the atmosphere.

This is how the terrestrial 'greenhouse' works: 287–249 = 38°C in round figures. The essential point, however, is that 51 units do reach the ground. Suppose now the cloudiness is increased. Up will go the albedo and the 'units' absorbed by the clouds, and so much less energy will reach the surface. It is true, of course, that fewer than 17 units will escape to space under such conditions. In sum total, however, the climate will

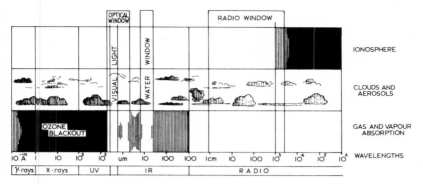

Fig 1 Electromagnetic spectrum and the atmosphere. Regions of partial transparency lined; scale of wavelengths logarithmic

become colder. In fact, massive, prolonged cloudiness could produce another ice age.[43]

It is not enough to consider average cloudiness only: its incidence is a vital factor as well. Daily experience reminds us that cloudy days are cool, but cloudy nights are relatively warm. If, therefore, there is more cloud by night than by day the mean temperature rises, and vice versa. This is, of course, because a clearer sky admits more sunshine by day, and a cloudy one prevents some of the ground heat escaping to space by night— it acts like a blanket.

The seasons and the winds

Another important factor is the inclination of the polar axis. Ours stands at an angle of 23° 27′ from the perpendicular to the plane of the ecliptic. A spinning body has 'gyroscopic stability'; its axis of spin preserves a constant orientation relatively to the fixed stars. As the Earth goes round the Sun, first the North and then the South Pole is tilted towards it.

This produces the variable length of days and nights (and so the seasons), as well as the climatic zones familiar from school geography. Where summer skies are relatively clear and the winter ones are cloudy, winters are relatively mild (as in Britain), for the winter's nights are longer than the days, so that the gain is greater than the loss. The sea serves further to temper the extremes of temperature. Water heats up very slowly and the sea absorbs a lot of heat (it has a high *specific heat*) during the summer, giving it off gradually during the winter. This is the secret of maritime climate. In the Sahara, where the skies are clear, the daytime heat may be sufficient to fry an egg in the sand, but night frost is not infrequent, even at the Equator.

The Earth's orbit is very nearly circular; its eccentricity is approximately 0.017, or less than 2 per cent. Nevertheless, at the present epoch it is somewhat closer to the Sun during the northern winter and the southern summer, and this does make a difference. The southern summers are hotter than those of the northern hemisphere, and the Antarctic ice-cap is more massive than the Arctic one. This will not always remain so, owing to the precession of the equinoxes. The geographical axis describes a cone about the normal to the orbital plane in 25,800 years, so that in 12,900 years the situation will be reversed with a corresponding change in the Earth's climates.

The eccentricity of the orbit of Mars is nearly eight times as large, with a correspondingly greater inequality between the seasons.

The rate of spin affects not only the length of days and nights, but also the air circulation. On a rotating sphere a point on the equator moves fastest, and the linear velocity of rotation declines towards the poles, where it drops to zero. Thus the winds, carrying the cold polar air, are deflected westwards in the northern hemisphere, and the other way round in the case of the warm air flow from the Equator. As these streams meet, they produce whirlpools, or cyclones and anti-cyclones. There is also a tendency for clear and cloudy weather belts to alternate, which is strongly marked on the fast-spinning Jupiter and Saturn.

'Life as we know it'

When in doubt about life on other worlds, the saving formula is to pronounce them unsuitable for 'life as we know it'. This life is based on water as the vital solvent; carbon as the chain-building element, important in the processes of polymerisation and polycondensation by which the large molecules, necessary to support the structure and transact the chemical business of life, are formed; nitrogen as a constituent of proteins; and phosphorus in the nucleic acids, which are guardians of heredity and instruments of control—in charge, as it were, of the brainwork of existence.[44]

There is no reason to believe that life could not develop on other chemical lines, at temperatures too low or too high for our type of biology. Our particular kind of life has evolved in the conditions peculiar to the Earth, and it is possible that it could have taken a different turn, save for some chance event in the early stages of its history. The condition of the Earth itself has evolved parallel and to some extent in response to life.

The so-called 'noble' gases are so inactive chemically that they do not ordinarily enter into chemical bonds even with themselves, and stay monatomic. Helium is the lightest of them (atomic mass 3 or 4), but neon (20), argon (40), krypton (84) and xenon (89) are heavy. They are also very abundant, both in the universe at large and in the Sun. These gases must, therefore, have been equally plentiful in the original atmosphere of the Earth. Today, however, with the partial exception of argon (which is formed by the radioactive decay of potassium-40), they are found only in minute traces. This means that the whole of the original atmosphere must have escaped to space—which necessitates high temperatures, because, being heavy, the noble gases would otherwise have out-stayed all the others.

The same must have happened on all the other terrestrial planets, including the Moon.

Yet plenty of gas remained underground, held by chemical bonding, in solution in the molten rocks (magma), and as pockets, large and small, in the partly-consolidated mass of the interior, bubbling away under the skin of the hardening Earth-crust. The corresponding surface volcanic activity must have been intense beyond anything we can readily imagine, with not just lakes but seas of lava, and huge quantities of volatiles oozing and blowing out of the interior. Steam accounts for some 90 per cent of the present-day volcanic exhalation and things must have been much the same then, so that shallow seas and wide temporary watercourses would soon begin to form under a hot and roiling atmosphere convulsed by furious thunderstorms.

This secondary volcanic atmosphere is believed to have been quite different from our present 'oxidising' air, in fact a reducing mixture of gases comparable to the envelopes of the giant planets, except for the high content of hydrogen in the latter. The main constituents would have been ammonia (NH_3), methane (CH_4), water vapour (H_2O), carbon dioxide (CO_2), phosphine (PH_4), sulphur dioxide (SO_2), and some minor volcanic exhalates. To begin with, this new atmosphere was rather thin and transparent to the Solar UV, which caused photo-dissociation, with the generation of free oxygen from water and CO_2—the hydrogen from the water as well as from methane and phosphine escaping to space. The formaldehyde reaction $CO_2 + 2H_2O = H.COH + H_2O + O_2$ also occurs quite naturally under the action of UV rays, and would further sustain this gradual oxygenation of the atmosphere, a process taken over at a much later stage by the photosynthetic action of green plants.

In any event, numerous experiments have shown that various organic compounds, including the amino acids (the building-blocks of proteins) and nucleotides (important in enzymes and nucleic acids), can arise spontaneously in such conditions under the action of UV radiation, electric discharge and radioactivity, all of which were present in considerable intensity on the infant Earth.

Its shallow waters became a kind of organic soup, where all manner of reactions were going on apace, including some cyclic ones in which the original reagents are reconstituted and multiplied in several stages. These were the forerunners of life, and in due course semi-organic structures, capable of self-replication and resembling our modern viruses, would have arisen and have begun to develop by natural selection in the struggle for survival.[45]

Such is believed to have been the origin of life. It came early, at least three aeons ago, but initial progress was very slow. It has taken the best part of 1,500 million years to evolve the modern eukaryotic cell, which for all its microscopic size is an amazing self-perpetuating complex of delicate chemical controls, checks and counter-checks, seemingly involving something beyond ordinary physics, all of which makes it a viable living unit.[46]

This great hurdle having been taken, the way was open to the development of larger organisms by the combination and differentiation of cells. Thus marine plants and animals arose, eventually to emerge on dry land about 500 million years ago. From our point of view two animal divisions are of the greatest interest: the arthropods and the vertebrates. It was, perhaps, touch-and-go as to which of the two would dominate the Earth.

The arthropods (insects, arachnids and crustaceans), however, remained small—chiefly, it seems, because their external skelton hampered growth and their tracheal system of respiration proved unsuitable for large-sized bodies. Still, sea-scorpions did reach a length of 9 feet and Carboniferous dragonflies managed a wingspan of a yard, so that perhaps this is not the whole story. Nevertheless, despite the early advances in social organisation among such arthropods as termites, ants and bees, they presented no serious challenge to the relatively enormous vertebrate animals.

But it was not so much size alone as awareness, organisation and co-operation, achieving an increasing degree of control over the environment, that were decisive in the struggle for the possession of the Earth. It was not inherited by the meek, but by the clever. The great problem both types of organism had to solve was the non-heritability of acquired characters, which entailed great waste in the loss of individual experience.

The difficulty was partly overcome by the development of collective memory, possibly involving telepathy, which we call *instinct*—a handy word that explains nothing at all. A parallel development was communication between members of a group, instruction of the young, and so symbolic language. This was not limited to the vertebrates, which did not on the whole progress far beyond warning cries and so-called 'phatic communication'. The researches of Carl von Frisch have revealed a far higher degree of abstract symbolisation among bees; and there is no doubt that ants and termites, too, can communicate some quite complicated information to each other. Nevertheless, their progress along these lines has been limited by the small size of their nervous systems, and they have been beaten to it by at least one species of gregarious vertebrate.

This began to emerge some 5 million years ago. It eventually developed a complicated system of symbolic communication, both vocal and visual in the form of 'graven images', corresponding at first to concepts and then to vocables. Abstraction and logical co-ordination began to evolve very rapidly, until the whole process of the evolution of the species has become externalised.[47] The collective knowledge and experience of generations exists outside the individual minds of its members, and it can develop at a steadily accelerating rate because of a complex social organisation. The result is absolute ascendancy over all other life, coupled with an extended measure of control over the environment—and its progressive spoliation.

The elimination of natural enemies and a high degree of control over infectious diseases has permitted the dominant species to multiply to a point where the resources of the planet can barely keep it going, and are threatening to fall short of the steadily increasing numbers. Unless the process is checked or reversed either by good planning or catastrophe, natural or unnatural, the total extinction of the species is a definite possibility.

Moreover, the technical powers at its disposal have become so great as to threaten the extinction of all life on the planet, and possibly even the destruction of the planet itself. This may seem a little far-fetched, but we do not really know what happened to that hypothetical planet between Mars and Jupiter half a aeon ago. Perhaps it was blown up accidentally by some technical error. This would indeed point a moral and adorn a tale, although personally I do not believe it very probable.

Exploration from space

Whatever the final outcome may be, happy or tragic, mankind's problems and troubles have become global. The Earth has to be, and increasingly is, considered as a whole.[48] The best way to do this is to survey it from outside, by spacecraft, just like Mars or Venus. Distant views of the Earth, from more than 20,000km away, are not very informative—there is too much cloud. Yet, although clouds remain a nuisance at all levels, from 'subspace' —between 100 and 1,000km above the surface—very clear and detailed pictures can be obtained (as was amply demonstrated by the *Gemini* and *Apollo* crews in the 1960s using hand-held cameras with colour-sensitive films and filters).[49]

On the ground we are rather in the position of a man who cannot see the wood for the trees. Perhaps a better analogy is aerial photography, revealing the buried foundations of ancient buildings of which not a stone remains on the surface, by the slight differences in the colouring of the overgrowing vegetation.

In many ways 1965 was an important year. Apart from the successes of the *Gemini* programme it saw the launching of the 85-lb telecommunication satellite *Early Bird*. Radio and especially television have a limited range, thanks to the curvature of the Earth and such obstacles as mountains. Like telegrams and telephone conversations, they can be conveyed by submarine cables; but these are difficult to lay, expensive in both installation and maintenance, whereas radio waves can be bounced off an Earth satellite and beamed over half the planet. For this purpose the 'telsat' is placed in a *synchronous* orbit: circling the Earth at 37,900km (22,300 miles) exactly along the Equator, completing one revolution in the same time as the Earth turns round, and thus sitting secure in the sky above a fixed point on the ground.

Things have progressed since the days of *Early Bird*. The

1,544-lb *Intelsat IV* has a capacity of 5,000 circuits and can handle 12 TV channels simultaneously.[50] There are more and more of these 'late birds'. Of course, they also require appropriate ground installations, but these are comparatively inexpensive. As a result we can be made almost instantly aware of a murder at Valparaiso or Yokohama, and can listen live to ministerial or presidential platitudes, which all serves to broaden the mind. One day even an ordinary citizen may be able to chat to his girl friend or a business associate on the other side of the world via a telsat, without more ado. The Earth is a small planet.

This is one practical spin-off from space flight. Another is the meteorological satellites such as *Nimbus*. Accurate weather forecasting, even for a day ahead and for such a small geographical region as the British Isles, requires reliable information on weather trends over a large area of the globe—in Britain's case mainly the Atlantic Ocean. Such information is pieced together from the reports of ships at sea, outlying islands, aircraft, and so on, which takes time and leaves many gaps. Now a weather satellite, circling the Earth in subspace (though still technically within the outer atmosphere), encounters no noteworthy air resistance and has a long life. Moving in a strongly inclined orbit with a period of a couple of hours, it keeps its TV eye on the cloud formations all over the globe, and what it sees becomes immediately available to the meteorological offices on the ground. Long-range forecasting is always a little chancy, but cyclones and anti-cyclones follow certain paths which vary with the seasons and some other circumstances, and reliable weather predictions for a month ahead should become possible with the aid of computers.

Of more immediate benefit is the early warning system for hurricanes and typhoons. Thus the great typhoon which devastated Bangladesh in 1970 and cost thousands of lives was spotted out at sea by an American weather satellite fully a week before it hit the shore. The ineffectiveness of the warning was due to the shortcomings of communication and organisation down below, not to any failure up above.[51]

There is no basic difference between aerial and subspace photography: the satellites fly higher than aircraft, and, obviously (weather permitting), can cover a larger expanse of the Earth's surface at a time. Such a photograph, even in black-and-white, is a kind of map, which can be corrected for the angle of viewing and illumination, as well as for the curvature of the globe. A colour photograph can be even more revealing. Certain features of geology, drainage, vegetation, etc, very difficult to detect for a ground investigator, stand out clearly in subspace views.

The early experiments demonstrated the various possibilities of a systematic subspace survey and gave rise to the robot TV *ERTS* (Earth Resources Technology Satellites) of 1972–3, and the more ambitious manned *Skylab*, whose crew of three was perio-dically relieved, lastly after 84 days, in 1973–4. The latter venture was not without its teething troubles but these were successfully dealt with by the men on the spot, thus demonstrating the possibility of effective repair work in airless space.

All these methods are fundamentally applicable to other planets, but in the case of the Earth we have the advantage of ground knowledge to assist us in the interpretation of what we see. Self-evidently, subspace photography can greatly improve the accuracy of the maps of poorly-known, difficult regions such as the mountain lands of Central Asia or the Amazon basin. Moreover, from such great heights the TV or camera 'eye' can penetrate to the bottom of shallow waters, while depth elsewhere is indicated by the varying intensity of colour. Currents, silt and pollution can similarly be brought to light.

Special techniques have been used in this connection, known somewhat pompously as 'multispectral photography', 'multi-spectral television' and 'multispectral scanning between UV and IR'—which in essence are nothing more than the use of filters, known for years in astronomical work. Special cameras have been developed for simultaneous exposure in three spectral regions, through relatively narrow-band, primary colour filters —red, green and blue. In multispectral scanning the range is extended beyond the optical window into the UV and IR.

IR photography and TV can be more revealing than the ordinary visual views. Since the eye does not respond to the IR, the picture has to be converted into false colours, vegetation (which is very bright in IR) being usually shown in red. The differences in hue correspond to the different conditions of growth, and may disclose the presence of fungus or virus diseases in crops. Moreover, the colouring is affected by the composition of the soil, and so may serve as an indicator of hidden mineral resources.

IR photographs can be taken in the Earth's own heat radiation, within the region of partial transparency between 3.5 and 5.5 µm and in the water window of 8–14 µm at night, and then converted into a visual image. The latter bears some resemblance to an ordinary photograph, but the differences in light and shade correspond to radiation temperatures. A lake will appear dark in a daytime IR photograph because it is then colder than its surroundings, but it will look bright in a night exposure. Thermal properties of the ground, warm sea currents, hidden seepages of volcanic heat, etc, can be discovered in this way.

The same technique can be used with microwaves, either passively or actively in radar. Microwaves can penetrate a thickness of solid rock, increasing with wavelength, and are unaffected by mist or cloud (unless electrified), which presents various advantages. Microwave pictures are also false by visual standards, but the contours and structure of the ground do not differ all that much from what is seen by the eye. More particularly, they can use the echoes from horizontally and vertically polarised radar, which yield somewhat different images depending on the nature of the rock formations, and so may be valuable to a geologist or mineral prospector.

A new development in false-colour photography is to isolate, in pictures taken in black-and-white with different colour filters, portions of equal density (defined by certain limits of light and shade) and then to overprint these equidensity views in different, arbitrary colours, which results in a futuristic kind of photograph reminiscent of the brilliant colour displays at the

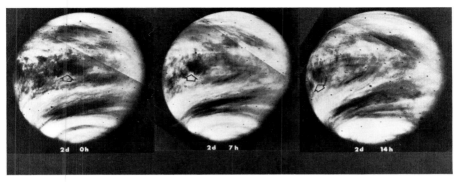

Plate 5 Mariner 10's UV filter captures the startling detail of the swirling cloud belts of Venus. Traced over a 14-hour period, the arrowed feature raced from east to west, contracting and changing its shape, at over 200 mph *(NASA/JPL)*

Plate 6 (top) Venera 9's photograph of the Venusian surface shows 'young' boulders with sharp, uneroded edges *(below)* The rocks seen by Venera 10 formed a different panorama: large pancakes, often fractured, resembling submarine lavas on Earth *(Novosti)*

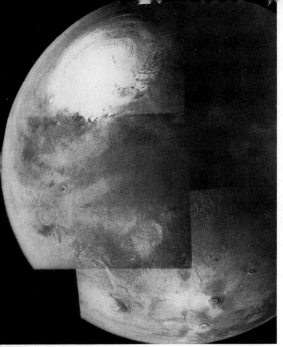

Plate 7 (left) Mariner 9 3-picture mosaic shows the northern hemisphere of Mars to a few degrees south of the equator. The north polar ice cap, shrinking as spring arrives, is at top; cloud wisps spiral due to Coriolis force. The region of great volcanoes is at bottom, with *Olympus Mons* at left. The vast extent of the northern lowlands shows clearly *(NASA/JPL)*

Plate 8 (below) Viking 1's orbiter takes a close-up of *Olympus Mons,* wreathed in mid-morning clouds. The giant volcano towers 23 km into the Martian stratosphere and its multi-ringed crater is 80 km across. Here the crater appears free of cloud, whose formations are best defined west of the mountain *(top left) (NASA)*

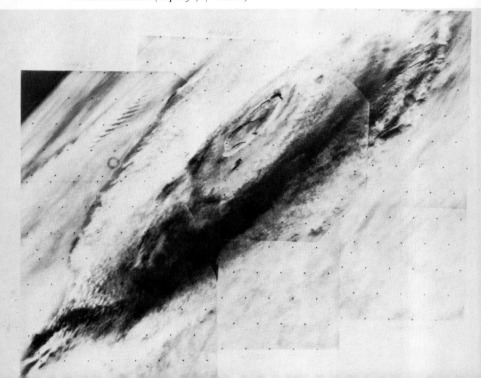

end of the film *2001—A Space Odyssey*. This can emphasise, say, marine depths and various features of ground structure, although the effects of shadows have to be taken into account.[52]

Gamma radiation from the ground can be monitored from an orbital vehicle, as has already been done on the Moon. This determines the radioactivity of the surface, and could lead to the discovery of uranium ores, vital to atomic power.

Microwave and radar 'photography' is astronomically valuable for the study of cloudy planets such as Jupiter or Venus, and has, in fact, been used for Venus with Earth-bound radar. The distance, however, is a little too great for the results to be wholly reliable. With a *Skylab* or an ERTS-type vehicle in orbit about Venus, we could do better.

Thus geography is fast becoming only a division of astronomy.

4

The Moon

The antiquity of the Earth–Moon system is an open question. As stated on p 15, the genesis of the Outer Planetary satellites is inapplicable to the Moon. It has been argued that the Moon may have been born from the Earth as a result of rotational instability enhanced by resonance with the Solar tides, the Pacific Ocean being the scar left by the Moon's departure. Yet, despite Sir George Darwin's impressive mathematics (1880), this idea has been shown to be untenable; and the differences in the composition of the lunar and terrestrial rocks revealed by the *Apollo* missions are a further nail in its coffin.[53]

The capture theory is now generally favoured. The situation has been investigated by H Gersternkorn (1955) and G J F MacDonald (1964) with the conclusion that the Moon must have been an independent planet for at least 3 aeons and only joined the Earth later—1.4 aeons according to the former, 1.75 aeons according to the latter.[54] A very close initial approach is assumed: MacDonald makes it 2.7 Earth-radii. This would mean an 8,000–fold increase in the amplitude of the present lunar tides,[55] producing fantastic tidal waves in which the oceans would literally roll over the continents, with a catastrophic disturbance of the Earth's internal equilibrium, earthquakes and volcanic eruptions of apocalyptic violence. If the Earth had any advanced order of life at that time this would certainly have been wiped out, only simple marine organisms being able to survive. The new life would have to start off if not from scratch at least from some very humble beginnings. Thus, instead of Earth being the Crown of Creation, the evolution of life on the planet may have been retarded by 2,000 million years.

Of this there is no present geological evidence. The oldest fossils are dated at about 3 aeons and consist of 'algal pavements', or *stromatolites*—a pretty primitive form of life. The trouble is that most sediments of such antiquity have been thoroughly granitised and their fossils obliterated. But the Ediacara fossils from South Australia and those of Charnwood Forest in Leicestershire, England (dated at about an aeon) show a fairly diversified marine fauna. The growth of stromatolites would indicate that Pre-Cambrian tides were $2\frac{1}{2}$–6 times stronger than now, so that the Moon would have been much closer then.[56]

Orbit and rotation

The gravitation of the Earth and the Sun draw level 260,300km from the Earth's centre. Beyond this limit the Sun's gravitation prevails—and that is where the Moon moves in an elliptical orbit, with its closest point to the Earth's centre (*perigee*) of 364,400km and its farthest (*apogee*) 406,730km away. The average distance works out at 384,400km (238,885 miles).

The Moon's orbit is always concave as seen from the Sun. It is a Solar orbit, strongly perturbed by the Earth's relatively large mass (81.3 times that of the Moon). Unlike the large satellites of Jupiter, Saturn and Uranus (which have their orbits close to the planet's equatorial plane). The plane of the Moon's path makes a constant angle of 5° 8′ 43.4″ with that of the ecliptic, which is itself inclined to the Earth's Equator at 23° 27′. This is why the Moon rides so high in the sky during the northern winter and sinks so low in the summer. In addition, the Moon's own equator subtends a constant angle of 1° 32′ not with its orbit but with the selfsame ecliptic—again in obeisance to the Sun.

Anyway, the Moon has been unable to resist the body tides raised in it by the Earth's gravity, and so has a captured or tied-up rotation (p 14). Its orbital and axial periods about the Earth coincide at 27 days 7 hours 43 minutes and 11 seconds. But they do not coincide very well. The rate of the Moon's spin is substantially uniform; its orbital velocity is not, because this orbit is an ellipse and is also subject to a 7-hour variation due to perturbations. Thus the spin now outruns, now lags behind the orbital motion. Instead of facing the Earth rigidly with the same side (as it would if its orbit were a circle), the Moon wobbles from side to side, or *librates*, as seen from the Earth. Owing to this and to the various inclinations, only 41 per cent of the Moon's surface remains permanently hidden from Earth.

Still, the Moon is somewhat heavier on the Earthward side, and behaves rather like one of those dolls which always stand up however tumbled over.

The Earth, whose phase as seen from the Moon is always complementary to the Moon's phase seen from the Earth (they add up to the full), does not hang motionless in the lunar sky either, but moves slowly about in response to the librations.

Because of the common motion of the Earth–Moon system round the Sun, the latter falls one-third of the circle behind the fixed stars each time the Moon turns round. Thus the Moon's Solar day, or the time from sunrise to sunrise, is longer than its true axial period referred to the stars, and averages 29 days 12 hours 44 minutes and 2.9 seconds. It varies slightly, as does Earth's Solar day, and for the same reasons; it also corresponds to the cycle, known as the *lunation*, in which the phases of the Moon recur.

The inclination of the Moon's polar axis (1° 32′) is so small that it cannot produce anything like the Earth's seasons or climatic zones, though it will have a slight effect close to the poles. The eccentricity of the Earth–Moon Solar orbit also results in a small fluctuation in the intensity of sunlight. Substantially, however, the day of the Moon is also the hot season and its night is the winter—each over a fortnight long.

As there is no atmosphere worth mentioning there can be no air temperature and no weather, although the Moon may be affected by *Solar* weather. If the splashes of molten glass found on the surface by *Apollo* astronauts *were* caused by a Solar flare of exceptional intensity, as suggested by Thomas

Gold, the effects of this weather could be rather drastic. This, though, is only a doubtful hypothesis. Gas clouds have been recorded on the Moon, and volcanic activity cannot be ruled out.

With these minor reservations the temperature of the Moon is that of its ground; it depends solely on the albedo and the altitude of the Sun above the horizon, which is determined by the time of day and the latitude of the place on the one hand, and by the angle of the slope on the other. A vertical cliff near the pole may face the Sun at right angles and be equally as hot as a patch of flat ground near the lunar equator with the Sun directly overhead. It may be boiling hot on the sunny side of a large boulder and freezing cold in its shade. All rocks and the lunar soil (*regolith*) are very poor heat conductors; but they do radiate according to their temperatures and some of this radiation will penetrate the shadows (as also does the light reflected by them), so that these shadows are neither quite so cold nor so black as they are painted.

Still, the Moon is a world of microclimates and harsh chiaroscuros.

On average the lunar surface reflects only 7 per cent of the light it receives. It is very nearly a black body, so that the Stefan-Boltzmann equation (which gives the absolute temperature in °K in function of 'blackbody radiation') can be applied to it 'in the raw' without any serious qualms, and the temperature measurements made from the Earth are reliable enough. The chart shown in Fig 2 gives a good idea of the general situation. At night the thermometer sinks quite rapidly to about −150°C, but subsolar temperatures may be as high as +120°C and higher.

Edison Pettit's observation of the effects of a lunar eclipse on the ground temperature has lost none of its pertinence since it was made on 28 October 1939. He chose a small area near the centre of the lunar disc and measured its blackbody temperature as 370°K (+97°C). Fifteen minutes after being covered by the Earth's penumbra the temperature dropped by 10°K (or C); and after an hour and 20 minutes, when the area

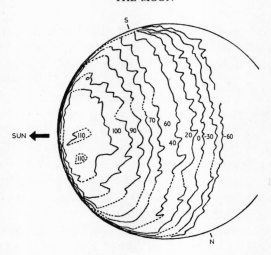

Fig 2 Lunar temperature chart. Distribution of temperatures on a gibbous Moon (after W M Sinton). Temperatures are given in °C; the arrow points towards the Sun. The jagged appearance of the isotherms reflects differences in the albedo and relief of the surface, untempered by convective circulation

entered the full eclipsing shadow, it was down to 198°K. Thereafter the decrease was gradual, showing a flow of heat from the deeper layers, to a bottom reading of 177°K (−96°C). The total eclipse ended after 3 hours 35 minutes. Two hours later the temperature was back at its original level.[57]

But the Moon's albedo is not uniform. Some areas are almost soot-black, while bright craters may reflect as much as 20 and even 40 per cent of the light they receive. They will absorb and radiate less heat in proportion. The same applies to the surface structure of different parts. During lunar eclipses, IR photography has revealed many 'bright' (warmer) areas. These have been found more particularly at the edges of the dark lunar plains (miscalled 'seas', or *maria*), and within some rayed craters such as Tycho and Copernicus, which stay 40–50°C warmer than their surroundings. This is attributed to structural differences; but the higher temperatures along surface fractures at the edges of some *maria* (the western 'shore' of

Mare Humorum in particular), appear to be due to magmatic heat seeping from the interior.

Penetrating below the surface, microwaves clearly show that at a depth of only about a foot (33cm) or two the thermometer never rises above freezing point, the maximum temperature lagging 3–4 days behind local noon. The subsoil of the Moon, like that of northern Canada or Siberia, remains in the condition of permafrost. At about 1m underground the temperature stays constant throughout the lunar day, some 35°C (K) above the surface average. If 220°K is taken as the latter (it varies with latitude and other factors), this makes the former 255°K (−18°C).[58]

On the other hand, the flow of heat from the interior has been measured in two 2-metre drill holes by the *Apollo-15* astronauts near the Hadley Rille, and again in two 233-cm ones near the crater Littrow on the *Apollo-17* mission with consistent results.[59] Recent measurements of radiation in centimetre wavelengths support these findings, and yield a thermal gradient about one-third that of the Earth's. This, it will be recalled (p 29), averages 2.5°C per 100 metres—higher in actively volcanic regions and lower in thick, stable geological 'shields'. The same is no doubt true of the Moon as well. A measurement at the western edge of the Sea of Humours would probably give a much higher figure, whereas it may be lower in some highland areas on the far side of the Moon.

None of the *Apollo* landing parties has been required to 'winter' on the Moon, but the orbiting command modules have regularly passed through its shadow without discomfort. Indeed, such thermal conditions should present no problems to a well-equipped base. Their predictability makes them much easier to deal with than the blizzards faced by an Antarctic or mid-Greenland scientific station.

The two-faced Moon

A recurrent feature of lunar topography is a walled hollow or enclosure, ranging from the tiny glassy pits caused by micrometeorite impacts on lunar boulders to huge plains ringed by 7,000-metre mountains. Seen through binoculars at half-phase the Moon looks pitted, like a thimble, and this is how it must have appeared to Galileo's astonished eyes in 1609. The face of the Moon is pock-marked—a cliché dating from the times when we knew only the 'near-side' of our natural satellite, in the pattern of whose natural markings a kind of human face could be made out with some help from the imagination. But since the 'farside' has been revealed to us by orbital spacecraft and photographically mapped in great detail, it is hardly appropriate to speak of '*the* face' of the Moon. It is two-faced, and the other 'face' is very different from the familiar Moon of our skies.

The Moon is not a perfect sphere, and its mean equatorial diameter measures 3,476km (2,160 miles), corresponding to a surface area of 37,960,000 square km and a volume of 2.199×10^{10} cubic km. It is a considerable world, which has much in common with Mercury and Mars, and is more Earth-like than it might at first seem.

If the Earth had lost its water and vegetation and were swept clean of sand and silt, it would look not unlike the nearside of the Moon: a pattern of bright and dark areas. As we have noted (p 29) the light-coloured sialic rocks are absent from the deep ocean beds, which are floored instead with dark basalts. To this extent the early astronomers who called the dark areas of the Moon *maria*, or 'seas', and the bright ones *terrae*, or 'lands', were geologically not far off the mark. Moreover the old names—*lunabase* for the dark lunar material, implying an analogy to Earth's basic rocks, and *lunarite* for the brighter highland rocks, a parallel with Earth's acid formations—although concealing a multitude of sins, have been largely justified by the subsequent close-up and on-the-spot investigations.

The Moon has no such handy reference level as that of our seas, nor even the 6.11–mb CO_2 pressure profile of Mars (p 122), so that the mean figure of the Moon is known but sketchily and its contour maps, prepared by different investigators and teams, are not in very good agreement. The laser retro-reflectors installed at the landing-sites of *Apollos 11*, *14* and *15* may help here, as well as in the detailed study of the relative movements of the Moon and Earth and their crusts (continental drift). They permit measurements accurate to within a few inches. But although the height of a lunar mountain above the surrounding ground can be determined with satisfactory accuracy by a simple geometrical method from the length of the shadows cast by it, all absolute heights are a little doubtful.

Not all lunarite features stand proud of the *maria*, but on average the latter lie $1\frac{3}{4}$km lower, so that they are depressed plains; and their flooring is basalt, just as in our oceans. The *terrae* have not been explored to the same extent. For one thing they are rough and have few safe landing sites to offer; for another they are much more varied. True, *Apollo 14* did touch down near *Fra Mauro*, which is at least a part-lunarite region, and *Apollo 16* in the ruinous enclosure of Descartes, actually in the Central Highlands. Yet it is questionable if even the latter is typical of terral material. Lunabase and lunarite grade into each other imperceptibly, and it is a fairly general rule that the highest parts of the ground are also the lightest, and vice versa.

True highland terrain was examined by the American soft-lander *Surveyor 7* on the outer slopes of Tycho. It picked up and weighed a rock, whose specific gravity was estimated from its shape at between 2.4 and 3.1.[60] The screes photographed by *Surveyor 7* showed a squarish granitic jointing, and proton analysis yielded compositions similar to that of syenite.

The orbital X and γ-ray surveys, as well as some of the rock samples picked up on the ground, suggest that the terral rocks are predominantly anorthosites, comparatively rare on the Earth and composed chiefly of plagioclase felspar.[61] No lunar granites have been discovered so far, but at least one rock sample was rhyolite lava of the same composition.[62]

In any event, it is well established that the proportion of

aluminium and silicon is higher in the *terrae* than in the *maria*, so that lunarite does correspond to our continental rocks.

It was calculated by J J Gilvarry in 1960 that if the original lunar magmas had contained the same proportion of volatiles, including water, as their terrestrial counterparts, the Moon ought to have possessed a copious atmosphere and real seas, covering the marial basins to an average depth of 2km. This condition would have endured for at least an aeon. His hypothesis had a cool reception, but it has never been faulted and may yet prove at least partly correct.

The 'seas' of the Moon

There are two types of *maria*. One is rounded (or more exactly polygonal, tending to hexagonal) and bounded by a steep mountain scarp which slopes gently outwards. In the irregular *maria* (described as 'epicontinental' by the German selenologist Kurd von Bülow)[63] there is no mountain girdle; the bordering *terrae* seem to dip into and under the lunabase, as is clearly shown by the coastal craters. The boundaries of such *maria* tend to be linear. But what with the confluence of adjacent lunabase plains it is not always easy to tell which is which.

The situation is best examined at full Moon, when ground relief casts no shadows and the differences of albedo stand out clearest.

The premier rounded 'sea' is *Mare Imbrium* (Sea of Rains). It measures 1,200km across and is girdled by some of the Moon's highest mountain ranges, with individual peaks exceeding 7km above the dark plain at their feet: the Jura, Alps, Caucasus, Apennines and Carpathians (all qualified as 'Lunar'). Only in the west is the bounding rampart pierced by the juncture with a still vaster epicontinental lunabase plain: *Oceanus Procellarum* or Ocean of Storms, of about the same area as the European USSR and overflowing in the south into *Mare Nubium* and *Mare Cognitum*.

Of special interest is the relatively small *Mare Orientale*

(Eastern Sea) on the Moon's western libration margin. Its central basin is some 500km across. It is surrounded by three rings of high mountains, with broad flatlands partly flooded with lunabase in between. An area of great disturbance extends all round the Mare for at least three times its diameter. The whole complex presents an appearance of freshness: this must be one of the youngest features of the lunar surface, and thus is the very opposite of the otherwise similar *Mare Nectaris* (Sea of Nectar).

Enormous sheet-flows of lava with typical lobate fronts and fingerlike extensions stand out clearly in the orbital photographs of *Mare Imbrium* and *Oceanus Procellarum* taken under oblique illumination. Similar basaltic floods are known on Earth, to take the Thulean Basalts (which cover an area of $2\frac{1}{2}$ million square km) or the Deccan Traps as examples. Moreover, the *maria* are the counterpart of our oceanic floors, some of which have been found to spread steadily, as basic lavas continue to pour out from zones of crustal weakness over the hot ascending edge of a convection cell. Such zones are marked by fractures and mid-ocean ranges, often cracked along the ridge. The ocean-floor spreading is the cause of continental drift, and is certainly responsible for the elevation of such mountains as the Andes and for the volcanic island arcs.[64]

The wrinkle-ridges of the lunar *maria* look very much like our oceanic ridges. At low magnification they resemble the crumpled skin on boiling milk, do not exceed the height of 1,000m, are often cracked or cratered at the top, and may pass over into crater-chains or surface fractures. It is clear that they owe their existence to periodic upwelling of basic lavas along deep-seated lines of crustal weakness. The fault systems in the south-eastern part of *Mare Imbrium* closely parallel those of the south-eastern Pacific, and the Apennines present an analogy to the Andean chain. The question arises whether the *maria* have also been spreading like our oceans.

Another feature typical of the *maria* are the so-called *rilles*. This is an unfortunate name because of the unintended association with the English word 'rill', and originates in the German

Rille, meaning groove. I will refer to them as *groove-valleys*. They do occur in the *terrae* as well but never far from large lunabase areas; nor are they all alike.

This requires a little excursion into geology. A crack in the ground is simply a fracture, but if there have been differential movements on its two sides it becomes a *fault*. An up or down movement yields a *dip fault*; a relative horizontal displacement of the two sides makes a *strike fault*. Both kinds of movement may, and often do, occur along the same fracture. There are swarms of fractures, which may be injected with magma and become *dykes*. Whole land blocks may be shifted or rotated, of which there are numerous examples on the Moon, more particularly in the Imbrian region of the Alps and the Caucasus.

A subsidence between two fractures makes a *graben*; when it is wide and its opposite banks move apart we have a *rift valley*, eg the Alpine Valley in the area mentioned above. The ground may also rise between parallel fractures, producing a kind of square ridge or *horst*. The fracture may be circular, giving rise to a *cauldron subsidence*; a circular uplift similarly yields a *dome*. A hill or ridge formed by extrusion from a fracture of viscous congealing lava is referred to as a *tholoid*.

A feature that is typical of the Moon is a *graben-groove*, which may extend for hundreds of kilometres and looks like the rut cut by a heavy wheel, passing impartially over hollow and hill, and thus obviously of deep-seated origin. Craters may pearl out along such a graben, as in the Hyginus Rille, or it may pass over into a crater-chain, a horst or a tholoid.

But there is a very different type of groove-valley or channel, known as the *sinuous rille* (see Plate 1). It has a winding, tortuous course, follows the slope of the ground and avoids vertical obstacles. It often originates in an elongated or pear-shaped crater and grows steadily thinner, or at least shallower, as it progresses, eventually petering out altogether. It is unmistakably a channel of flow.

Now there are no proper *maria* on the farside of the Moon at all. A few minor lunabase plains encroach on it just over the edge of the libration zone. *Mare Australe* (the Southern Sea) is little more than a jumble of lunabase-floored craters; *Mare Moscoviense* (the Sea of Moscow), discovered by *Luna 3*, although comparable in size to *maria* like *Mare Nectaris*, is only partly lunabase. On the other hand the farside abounds in large rings with lunarite floors, up to 500km in diameter, which have been christened *thalassoids* ('little seas'). *Mare Ingenii*, in the south polar region of the farside, is a thalassoid with a part-lunabase floor.

I have found only one short sinuous channel on the farside, and graben-grooves are equally scarce.

Craters, bulwark plains and the like

The word 'crater' has become associated with a volcanic vent, or a pit excavated by an explosion. But in thinking of lunar, Mercurian, Martian or even terrestrial craters it is best to free ourselves from any explanatory connotations and regard them primarily as land forms which may be due to a variety of causes.

On the Moon there are shallow and deep craters, craters with raised walls, and rimless pits. Some have flat floors; those of others are cracked and rumpled. A hill or group of hills may rise from the centre of the floor. These hills often have summit pits, like Vesuvius-type volcanoes or spatter-cones. The central peak is almost invariably lower than the girdling wall. It may be replaced by another crater, sometimes beautifully concentric as in Hesiodus A, which looks like a wide-brimmed hat. Convex floors are rarer; internal domes are common. Summit craters apart, the crater floor is characteristically depressed below the surrounding country—but there are exceptions to this rule as well,[65] and the 80km Wargentin is filled with up-welling lava almost to the brim, forming a kind of table mountain.

In 1964–5, *Rangers 7* and *9* first revealed numerous soft-shouldered depressions, each with a funnel-like pit in the middle. These seem to be either swallets or gas-escape channels. But small sharp, clear-cut craterlets of the same type exist, and not necessarily on *mare* floors. There are quite a few of

them on the peaks and ramparts of the great mountain ring of
Tsiolkovsky and thereabouts on the farside. Parts of the country
about the north pole of the Moon is peppered with what the
American selenologist J E Spurr has described as 'blowholes'.[66]
In this case the material is chiefly lunarite, but blowholes are
typical of lunabase-flooded depressions, such as the great trough
of the Alpine Valley (p 64) and the level floors of large rings,
where the craterlets are often perferentially oriented. They seem
to be due to the escape of gases from extensive lava flows.

Craterlets of this kind often form continuous chains, strung
like beads over a visible or suspected surface fracture. There is
a readily observable example of such a chain running along
the north-eastern walls of the great 145km enclosure of Ptole-
maeus near the centre of the Earthward hemisphere. Not that
chains of larger craters are lacking. There are also interesting
pairs of very similar craters, evenly spaced, the northern one
somewhat the larger of the two. Archimedes-Eudoxus, Aristillus-
Autolycus and Godin-Agrippa are the best known of these.[68]

Chains of craterlets often wreath the ramparts of large rings
and/or run down along them—a development well known in
terrestrial volcanoes. Nor are conical mountains with a summit
crater unknown on the Moon, although they are comparatively
inconspicuous, swamped by the large, broad rings. On the
other hand, lava flows on the walls and floors of the rings are
common and undisputed.[69] Their wall terraces often cradle
flat 'lakes' of lava; in most cases the floor is a smooth plain, but
those of Hevelius and Gassendi are rough and seamed with
fractures ('turtle-back' craters).

These are very large formations, but some small craters
display similar features. There is, however, a general progression
of appearance with increasing size. The smallest craters are the
most circular in outline, which becomes more ragged and
polygonal with increasing diameter. There is a special class of
very neat bowls, 100m to 1km across, looking as though they
have been machined to a pattern—but other craters of the same
size are rough and bouldery. Flat dish-craters with low walls
also occur, a special type of which has been described by

Gilbert Fielder as 'elementary rings': the circular wall is equally steep on both sides and there is no central depression.[70]

But in most rings over 10km the walls are characteristically raised at the edge, dipping steeply inward and sloping gently to the outside. They usually have a gentle step leading to the level patch in the middle, as in a saucer; there may or may not be a central peak. In smaller craters the walls are plain and single, but with diameters between 20–100km they develop multiple ridges and terraces, eventually becoming whole mountain ranges as the size increases. Flat-floored rings 50–100km wide are sometimes described as *crater-plains*, and still larger ones as *bulwark-plains*.

There are also the thalassoids. One of the latter is *Mare Ingenii*, which with some of its neighbours is rather exceptional. Its inner slopes are radially ridged and gullied, like water-scoured mountain sides. Another rare development is spiral walls, as in the crater Sabine.

Haloes and rays

Many small craters have bright or dark haloes. The former have often been recognised as boulder fields, but have in some cases been described as 'crystalline' by orbiting astronauts. Dark haloes are limited to small craters, but many large ones have broad dark bands on their inner walls, sometimes overrunning these—association with chains of blowholes is suspected. Bright haloes are common around large rings, of which Tycho is literally a shining example. More often than not they compose a star-like pattern of rays, sometimes preferentially orientated (Proclus) and tangential to the crater walls.[71] In some cases a connection with surface fractures is apparent, but the rays seem to consist of glass marbles or glass splashes—common in the lunar regolith.

The bright, long rays (up to 1,000km) are seemingly unaffected by surface relief, characteristic of Tycho and described as 'Tychonic'. 'Copernican' rays, on the other hand, are much darker, tangled, looped or comet-shaped, and obviously obstructed by quite low heights, such as wrinkle-ridges. The divorce between the two kinds is not absolute: all rays tend to be dimmed in crossing lunabase. Most bright and rayed craters are on the nearside of the Moon.

Even casual inspection shows that mountain rings and craters must differ greatly in age. Some look clear-cut and fresh; others of similar structure are subdued, ruinous, bearing witness to long-sustained destructive processes. Rays and haloes are particularly associated with fresh appearance; they seem to be the first to yield to the tooth of time. Yet it seems that not all craters began their existence rayed or haloed: these features are lacking in many well preserved formations.

Crater walls are typically lunarite, even in the *maria* (with some doubtful exceptions such as Landsberg and Rheinhold). Mid-marial craters such as Timocharis or Aristillus are instructive because they stand alone. The ring is perched atop a wide gentle dome, furrowed by radial gullies, which run far out into the surrounding plain. Aristarchus displays feathered ash-flows on its outside slopes and is very bright. It is, in fact, the brightest spot on the Moon—but its rays are of the Copernican type. This recalls terrestrial shield-volcanoes associated with basic lavas, such as Askja in Iceland, except that the latter is much smaller.[72] But there are giant shield-volcanoes on Mars.

The lunar globe

It used to be the fashion to think of the Moon as an inert, rigid body, which has never had a molten interior, and whose surface has been shaped by external forces. As we have seen on p 59, however, the flow of internal heat in the subsurface rocks of the Moon is quite appreciable, with a thermal gradient about $\frac{1}{3}$ of the terrestrial, say 8°C per km. Thus at a depth of 100km below the surface the temperature would be some 800°C, very much as at our Moho.

At such temperatures basalts begin to melt, or at any rate become plastic, and isostasy must be expected to operate on the Moon, the denser rocks tending to sink and the lighter ones

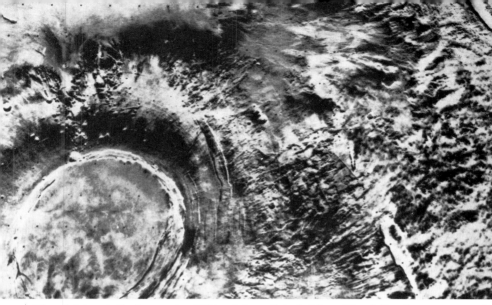

Plate 9 (above) Early morning *Viking 1* shot of *Arsia Mons* ('South Spot'), another of the great volcanoes of the *Tharsis* region, showing several wispy clouds *(NASA)*

Plate 10 (below left) An African river from 21,000 feet, darkly limned by forest, crowding into the river valley . . . *(Department of Lands and Surveys, Uganda)*

Plate 11 (below right) . . . and a Martian river channel in *Nirgal Valtis*. *(NASA)* Its darkness is not all shadow, and closely resembles the appearance of the African river

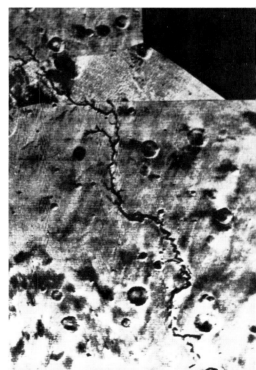

Plate 12 Portion of the central ridge, up to 2 km high, in *Valles Marinerius* on Mars, showing dismemberment by water erosion (north side) and avalanche shoots to the south *(Mariner 9) (NASA)*

Plate 13 Dramatic *Viking 1* photograph showing a teardrop 'island', presumably shaped by water in the planet's past, in the *Chryse* region. The furthest outlines of the large craters have also been blurred by erosion. This was the scheduled landing-site for *Viking 1*, but it proved to be so rough in reconnaissance pictures like this that the landing was postponed and shifted elsewhere *(NASA)*

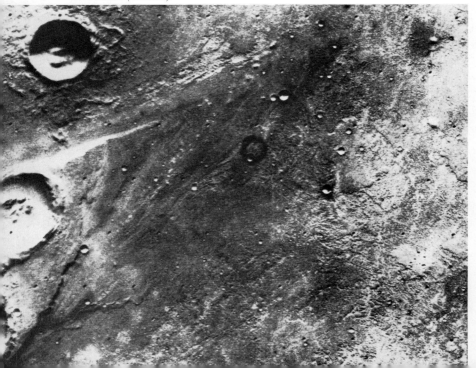

to rise. True, the differences in weight will be muted by a sixfold reduction, so that lunar rocks will be able to support far greater masses without yielding, making isostatic adjustments slower and less effective. But this works both ways, and the same pressure of, say, a rising column of magma will have a heaving power six times greater than on the Earth. This may be one reason why lunar lava flows have been so extensive and tholoids (p 64) so numerous. The latter will also be favoured by the tendency of the lava to froth up, and so cool by expansion, under low atmospheric pressure, developing a rigid crust under whose cover tholoidal extrusion can proceed.

We have also seen that even at the present time, which appears to be one of selenological quiescence, there exist on the Moon hot pockets close to the surface, so that volcanic activity can be expected. Indeed, early records apart, it has been reliably observed in recent times. On 3 November 1958 and 23 October 1959 the Russian astronomer N A Kozyrev, using a 50-inch reflector, saw red glows and an emission of gas (of which he obtained spectral records indicating high temperatures) near the centre of the bulwark-plain of Alphonsus. In the course of mapping work, at the Lowell Observatory, USA, on 30 October 1963, A Greenacre and E Barr noticed reddish-orange glows declining to ruby-red in the Cobra-head and along the rim of the neighbouring mountain-ring of Aristarchus. The glows endured for 25 minutes and reappeared on 28 November, when they were also witnessed by John Hall, Director of the Observatory. This time they were succeeded by a blue haze, often reported in Aristarchus and some other craters. The effect remained observable for 1 hour 15 minutes.[73]

Lunar vulcanism is generally weaker, owing to the greater depths at which high magmatic temperatures are reached. This also applies to moonquakes, of which we now have an ample record from the seismometers installed at the landing sites of *Apollos 12, 14, 15* and *16* and still operative. The last-mentioned has the most sensitive equipment and registers about 3,600 shocks every year. The *Apollo 14* site follows with 1,600 and the other two with 650.[74]

Genuine moonquakes are readily distinguishable from meteoric impacts (which, incidentally, are far less frequent than expected). Forty-one active moonquake zones have been located. The quakes are mainly of the deep-seated type, not unknown on Earth, with foci 600–1,000km below the surface. The seisms show a definite association with the varying tidal action of the Earth at the perigee and apogee (p 35).

The mean radius of the Moon is 1,738km, and the suppression of 'shake-waves' within the innermost 700km indicates a molten condition. There is an uncertain discontinuity at about 60km below the surface, and minor variations in the velocity of seismic waves in the top layers. On no evidence at all, the temperature at the centre is put at 1,500°C,[75] which seems much too low and a hangover from the inert-Moon idea. It is, however, clear that the inner structure of the lunar globe resembles that of the Earth.

This conceals an awkward problem.

Lunar rocks differ from ours and from typical meteorites in their relatively high proportions of titanium, zirconium, haffnium, yttrium and chromium, and are low on sodium, potassium and rubidium.[76] But there is no indication of a lower content of iron; if anything quite the reverse. Iron and other heavy metals would fuse and tend to flow down towards the centre of the globe. If so the Moon's core must be nife, as with the Earth, although somewhat smaller than the Earth's in relation to the total radius. Thus we would have some 60km of sial, followed by 980km of sima and finally 700km of nife. The corresponding densities cannot be less than 2.7, 3.2 and 7.5 respectively. With a mean density of 3.342, the Moon has a mass of 7.351×10^{22}kg. Now the masses of the three zones as defined above are: nife, 1.085×10^{22}kg; sima, 5.936×10^{22}kg; sial, 0.578×10^{22}kg; and this adds up to 7.599×10^{22}kg, which is 0.248×10^{22}kg too much. The real excess should be a good deal more, as we have put all our densities at the lowest possible values, disregarding further decimal places, and taken no account of the inevitable downward increase in density due to geological fractionation and compression. Yet the real mass of the Moon falls substantially short of the mark, and this requires an explanation.

Moreover, from the deformation of the crater walls J E Spurr has inferred[77] that the diameter of the Moon at the time of their formation was some 50 per cent larger than now, so that the Moon has evolved from a lower to a higher density and smaller size through enormous volcanic gas exhalation. I suspect some exaggeration here, but the idea is far from foolish: the Earth's atmosphere and hydrosphere has also come from the interior (p 43).

To understand the situation, let us consider the origin and development of the Moon.

It seems to have begun as a loose aggregation of small cold bodies: dust, meteors, 'ices' and gases—rather like an extra-large comet. As the growing mass contracted under its own gravity it became heated, a process assisted by the simultaneous decay of short-lived radioactive substances, long since eliminated. According to Kuiper[78] the original heat from this source was ten times as high as today. Heating would progress from the inside outwards, producing a molten metallic core encased in rock slag, with the volatiles driven off towards the surface.

But the expulsion of volatiles from the interior is governed by compression and temperature, both of which would be lower than in the larger mass of the Earth, the latter because heat is generated, other things being equal, in proportion to the volume, and so to the cube of the radius, and radiated off the surface in proportion to the square of the radius. Thus smaller masses will be less hot and cool faster. The conclusion is that large quantities of volatiles remain locked inside the Moon, in a vast system of underground caves at a moderate depth below the surface. This should not surprise us: there are underground lakes and rivers beneath the parched sands of the Sahara, and on the Moon the permafrost seal helps to bar the escape of water to the surface.

The degassing of the Moon has not ceased. On 21 February 1971 a large gas cloud, lasting nine hours, was registered by the *Apollo 14* instruments. An even larger cloud was recorded at both the *Apollo 12* and *14* sites on 7 March 1971. This was 99 per cent water vapour and seems to have come from a geyser eruption in *Oceanus Procellarum*.[79] The total emission must have been considerable. Both events have been explained away as gas escapes from the abandoned equipment, but whether this hypothesis is wholly convincing is another matter.

The well-authenticated 'transient lunar phenomena' (TLP or LTP)[80] also involve gas emission; and 90 per cent of terrestrial volcanic exhalation is steam. In lunar conditions any liquid water is technically superheated and will flash into steam, in a geyser or 'phreatic' eruption, on reaching the surface. This could produce at least some minor craters.

In fact, the Moon does possess a very thin residual atmosphere. The Russian 'Moon-crawler' *Lunokhod 2* has reported a daytime and twilight radiance of the lunar sky which is surprisingly strong in the visual wavelengths, though weak in the UV.[81] This would indicate dust or crystals but a certain amount of gas is needed to keep them up, and this may be derived partly from the interplanetary gas and partly from the interior. The small mass spectrometer installed by *Apollo 17* has recorded significant amounts of argon-40, probably generated by the decay of the radioactive potassium-40, with a diurnal variation suggesting sorption. The spectrometer carried by *Apollo 15*'s orbiting command module detected molecular nitrogen, ascribed to volcanic sources, near *Mare Orientale*.[83]

Study of the irregularities in the flight of lunar orbital craft (*Orbiter 5* in particular) has revealed the existence of *mascons* (mass concentrations) in the principal *maria*, no doubt due to large masses of heavy rocks on or near the surface. The distribution of mascons suggests a connection with convective cells in the lunar mantle (p 30), and they can be readily accounted for by the partial collapse of the honeycomb of caves and its invasion by basic magmas from the interior. The most probable cause seems to lie in the body tides raised by the Earth, either during the close encounter with the Moon before its capture, as a result of the originally more eccentric orbit, or during periods of increased selenological activity.

Asteroidal impacts have been suggested as the origin of the *maria*, and it is true that the appearance of *Mare Orientale* does at first sight fit this interpretation rather well.[84] It is, however, difficult to reconcile with the virtual absence of *maria* from the farside, and the long sequence of events in *Mare Imbrium* revealed by the stratification in the Hadley Rille and in the faces of the Lunar Apennines. The latter show great series of seemingly undisturbed strata, which have become tilted and uplifted into mountains without any sign of great violence. These peaks are certainly not built up of chaotic rubble thrown out of an explosion pit.

The impact theory and its difficulties

As stated, walled enclosures are the prevalent theme of lunar topography, and these must have been formed by either internal or external forces, the latter in the form of meteoritic impact. The two explanations are not mutually exclusive; in fact, both must be true to some extent. But the latter idea draws strength from the prejudice in favour of an inert Moon and is still widely held among scientific officialdom,[85] often in the teeth of overwhelming evidence against it.

On Earth the Meteor or Barringer Crater in Arizona is only 1.2km across. The 15-km Rieskessel in Germany may be an impact feature. There are a few other candidates to the same origin, but geological opinion is far from unanimous about some of these. Oddly enough, the only fall of a large meteorite that was actually recorded, in the Tunguska in 1908, devastated a large area of Siberian forest but left no crater at all. On the other hand, the volcanic collapse *caldera* (a structure resulting from the caving-in of a volcano or dome) of Ngorongoro, Tanzania, measures 29km in diameter. We also have the gigantic ring-volcanoes referred to on p 30, which rival not only the largest bulwark plains of the Moon but *Mare Imbrium* itself. Most of these terrestrial examples are very ancient and,

unlike their lunar counterparts, poorly preserved. They seem
to belong to the early times when the 'magmatic phase' was
stronger in the mountain-building processes.[86]

Certain features of the lunar rings are badly out of joint
with the meteoritic theory. Many of the large enclosures, for
instance, have contiguous walls. Where these intersect the
junction is sharp and clear, and sometimes the old wall can be
traced on the floor of the later ring. This points to gentle subsidence rather than a catastrophic genesis. And the overlapping
crater is almost invariably smaller than the overlapped one,
which means that every successive impact would have had to
have been less powerful than the one before. This is readily
understandable in terms of declining internal forces, but it
puts an unbearable strain on the meteoritic interpretation.[87]

The latter assumes that the meteorite strikes the surface with
a velocity of some tens of kilometres per second,[88] although a
body falling from infinity to the Moon's surface would only
reach the escape velocity of 2.38km per second. The differences
in the orbital velocities of bodies co-orbiting the Sun with the
Moon would not be much greater either, so that we start off
from an exaggeration. Yet the energy of the impact is supposed
to be converted into heat, with the intense temperatures of the
order of 10^7°C found in a nuclear explosion.[89] As a result, most
if not all of the meteorite itself, plus some of the rock at the
point of impact, is vaporised, excavating the crater by the
explosive decompression of these intensely hot gases. It is all
over in a millisecond, and yet huge masses of rock are supposed
to be melted in the process.

Thus it was estimated at the Fourth Lunar Science Conference
that 700 cubic kilometres of lava have been generated by
impact in the crater Copernicus.[90] But according to Thomas
Gold (1955), himself a supporter of the meteoritic theory, 'the
transport by conduction of heat cannot account for more than
a very thin layer of liquefaction'.[91] Only a shallow glazing can
be expected, and this is in fact what we find in the Barringer
Crater and in nuclear explosion pits. Moreover, in the case of
Copernicus and other similar mountain-rings, lava continued to

flow from obvious vents and fissures long after the excavation of the crater. It would thus have been within easy reach from the start, and the impact would only be a triggering cause.

This is not to say that there are no meteoritic craters on the Moon, the Earth and other planets: they undoubtedly exist, but the assertion that they have been a primary factor in the development of planetary surfaces is at best not proven. Great volcanic eruptions, such as that of Krakatoa in 1883 or of Katmai in 1917 would in lunar conditions produce ray systems as extensive as, if not more than, those of Tycho or Giordano Bruno. Phreatic action has already been mentioned as another possible mechanism of crater formation.

Magma is not the only deformable material that can be intruded through or between stratified rocks—now known to exist on the Moon—so as to form dykes, sills, or laccoliths. Any 'incompetent rock' will do for this purpose: there are limestone and sandstone dykes. More particularly, salt and ice behave somewhat like magma. An ice laccolith can raise a dome which will then cave in as the ice melts or evaporates, forming a neat crater: this is known as a *pingo*. Some lunar or Martian craters may be *pingos*.[92]

Fracture grids

In addition to its circular forms, lunar topography has linear systems of lines of weakness, or *tectonic grids*, along which land movements tend to recur. Such master-fractures are known in terrestrial geology (Hobbs, Vening Meinesz, de Sitter)[93] and three such grid systems (Firsoff, Fielder)[94] are recognised on the Moon. They usually align with the walls of the bulwark plains, as well as the 'shores' of the *maria*.

The arcuate or linear mountain ranges along the latter bear a superficial resemblance to the Alpine mountains of the Earth, but there is no evidence of water or ice action on a large scale among them; and it is doubtful if folding has played any important part in their elevation. The strata exposed in the faces of the lunar Apennines are nowhere bent or twisted. The mountains consist of shattered, variously shifted and tilted fault-blocks, which have been lifted by isostasy in compensation for the subsidence of the heavy filling of the *maria*—and also by the pressure of the lunarite *terra* against the lunabase of the *mare*, either spreading or acting as a stable shield during the contraction of the lunar globe.[95]

This is not greatly different from the upheaval of the Andes along the Pacific coast. Also like the Andes, some peaks in the lunar Apennines (especially in the Caucasus and the Alps) are volcanoes with summit craters. The mountains on the far side of *Mare Australe* are also volcanic.

A related and specifically lunar form is what I have described as 'cellular mountains',[96] represented by the Leibnitzes and the Doerfels. These comprise the greatest relative heights of the Moon, standing over 10km from foot to head. The system is made up of squarish bulwark plains, having common walls with peaks rising at their meeting points.

Erosion, ice and water

The 'terrorist geology' of impact has had its greatest success in application to small-scale structures.

At the present epoch and for many millions of years past the lunar surface has been pelted by a constant stream of fast projectiles: short-wave photons, Solar Wind, cosmic rays and micrometeorites. These nibble at the rocks at an estimated rate of 1cm per 10 million years. There may. be other causes of erosion: rapid temperature changes during eclipses and/or sorption and desorption of gases, which operates even under extremely low pressures.[97] During the day the lunar surface is charged to a potential of $+10$ volts, which changes at night to -100 volts. This is attributed to bombardment with Solar protons, but similar changes can be produced by sorption and desorption and the photo-electric effect, without any protons, ought to suffice for a daytime positive charge.

However, at none of the landing sites is bedrock exposed, save for isolated boulders. Everything is smothered under a variable pall of highly cohesive soil, the *regolith*, with a soft, dusty top layer. The depth of the regolith appears to be 2–3 metres, with coarser rubble underneath, consolidated into breccia at still deeper levels. The regolith is made up of fragmentary material of micron-to-centimetre size. There are several kinds of it: individual rock pieces, microbreccias, fused glasses, either amorphous or in the form of rounded 'marbles' (some of which have a teardrop shape indicative of atmospheric drag at formation), and black adhesive dust—at least in the *maria*—resembling coal-dust but shown to consist of tiny globules of fused basalt—no doubt a splutter effect.

The regolith is layered. The 260-cm core taken at the *Apollo 15* site contained no less than 57 layers, thought to span a period of 2,400 million years.[98]

The composition of the regolith varies somewhat from place to place and layer to layer, and so does the depth of the soft overlay. The latter was thickest on the rims of small depressions near the *Apollo 12* site, but thin at *Apollo 11*'s Tranquillity Base. Mention must here be made of the Russian *Luna 9*, which landed at the western edge of the Ocean of Storms, almost within range of the disturbance halo of the Eastern Sea (p 62). A foot of the probe appears in the photograph, and instead of scooping up some of the surface material, like other probes, its impact seems to have produced a bundle of thin radial fractures, running through a 'reindeer-moss' of stone which must be hard and brittle.[99]

As yet we know only a tiny portion of the Moon's surface.

The fact that the *maria* and other lunabase areas have well-defined boundaries, despite the overlying regolith, indicates that the latter has been derived from the local country rock—as the micro-erosion processes mentioned above would lead one to expect. But the layering clearly includes foreign material. In the Alps some sinuous channels stand out clearly in the lunabase valleys, but are barely visible higher up in the light-coloured mountains. These are volcanic, so that the overlay must be volcanic ash.

The lunar soil is being constantly churned up by micro-impacts, a process described as 'gardening'. This ought to be uniform all over the Moon, but apparently it is not. The material scooped up from *Mare Crisium* by *Luna 16* seems to have experienced very little 'gardening'.

The radioactively determined ages of lunar rocks are 1–4 aeons, but oddly enough the regolith, supposed to be derived from them, is often an aeon or two older than they. The simplest explanation seems to lie in an admixture of meteoric matter, for the most part unrecognised because its composition has altered over the ages—the present meteorites being of comparatively recent origin.[100]

Light elements, including carbon, have been leached out of the surface by the 'gardening' and by radiation, as the increase in the proportion of carbon with depth indicates.[101] No traces of life, past or present, have been discovered—hardly surprisingly, given the present condition of the Moon. Nevertheless, A L Burlinghame's study group has found in a Tranquillity sample small amounts of organic compounds, including traces of higher hydrocarbons, which in their opinion could not be attributed to *Apollo 11*'s retro-rocket exhaust.[102]

It is commonly assumed that things on the Moon have always been as they are today. Yet the vast lava flows in the *maria* could not have occurred without a parallel emission of great amounts of gas. 'Geyser eruptions' or not, the lion's share of this gas must have been water vapour, as in our volcanic exhalations. Any suggestion of water on the Moon—or on any other planets—arouses something like pious horror, about which there is nothing scientific. Hydrogen and oxygen being the most abundant active elements in the universe, water is an extremely common substance. Anyway, at the time the lava fields were forming the Moon would have acquired a substantial atmosphere, and if the barometric pressure had risen over 6.1 millibars liquid water could have appeared on its surface. The only question is, have we any supporting evidence for this? And the answer is yes.

The *New Scientist* of 1 August 1974 (p 230) notes:

In 1972 Dr S O Agrell of Cambridge University reported the detection of minute amounts of goethite $Fe_2O_3H_2O$ in samples of *Apollo 14* breccias. Now three workers from the US Geological Survey, Denver, report rusty streaks of the mineral in another lunar sample (*Science*, vol 185, p 346). They believe it to be original and hence to represent the presence on at least parts of the Moon of water in larger quantities . . . than petrologists have deduced from other lunar material.

The isotopic composition of this water indicates non-terrestrial origin, so that it cannot be explained by contamination in storage.

The sinuous channels, or rilles (p 64) have been explained away rather lamely[103] as collapsed lava tubes. A few of them may be, for these features vary greatly in structure; but typically they look nothing like a collapsed lava pipe. R E Eggleton and H G Moore of the US Geological Survey have studied 25 sinuous rilles and confirmed that they have all the characteristics of water channels.[104] Under the conditions envisaged, precipitation in the form of rain or snow is unlikely to have been of any significance, whence the lack of tributary streams. (But even this is less than certain; I have traced in the Apennines some thin channels leading into the Conon Rille.) In general water would have assumed the character of a volcanic material, like lava; in breaking the permafrost seal it would emerge copiously from hot springs on the sides of active volcanoes, and this is precisely what we find.

A sinuous channel originates in an elongated crater on a side or at the foot of a mountain ring or partly volcanic mountains. It progresses downslope, simultaneously decreasing in depth and volume (and usually width as well), as a stream of water would in conditions of great aridity under a low atmospheric pressure.

The Conon Rille starts from a 'lake'. In fact there are quite a few such 'lakes' with clearly defined shores: in *Mare Orientale* and in the north-western part of *Oceanus Procellarum*, where the floods, however temporary, must have assumed the pro-

portions of a real sea, although nothing like as deep or extensive
as Gilvarry's (p 62). *Mare Ingenii* also seems to have cradled a
large lake, and the bright cloudy patterns on its floor suggests a
deposit of silt. A sinuous rille flows into it, and we may re-
member (p 67) its gullied inner walls.

Sinuous channels are characteristic of lunabase plains. The
Bode Rille, however, is a mountain feature, and there are some
thin sinuous channels arising in the Rook Mountains, running
into a lunabase-filled rift valley and continuing along its floor.
Such a feature could not possibly be a collapsed lava pipe, for
the mountains are lunarite and the valley is lunabase, so that the
lava must have abruptly changed its composition where the two
meet. Moreover, the mountains antedate the rift valley.[105]

Although an atmosphere would have tempered the present
extremes of temperature, the lunar nights would have been very
cold. During such a 'water period' the night side of the Moon,
its polar regions and high mountains would have been white
with hoarfrost. There are indeed signs of local glaciation. Some
of the NASA investigators have noticed this in the neighbourhood of the crater King on the farside,[106] but I think Riccioli
and the 'aureole' of *Mare Orientale* present some even better
examples of glaciation.

There are also curious aprons on the outer side of Tsiolkovsky's great ring on the farside, and there is nothing quite
like them anywhere else on the Moon, although photographs
by the *Viking* orbiters show them to be not uncommon on Mars.
They may be landslides, but they bear a suggestive resemblance
to the 'rock glaciers' of Alaska. A rock glacier is a glacier
completely buried under rock debris so that the underlying ice
is not exposed, but continues to flow. A terrestrial covering
could hardly have preserved a lunar glacier from evaporation,
but a thick coat of volcanic ash and compact regolith could
have done the trick.

The overheating cycle

For the present purpose it is immaterial whether the *maria* were formed by impact or internal forces, or some combination of both. The essential point is the intense gas exhalation following the event. Personally I favour the view that the Moon has its orogenetic cycles (p 31), its interior becoming periodically overheated. This results in 'geological rejuvenation', intense volcanic and tectonic activity, expressed more particularly in collapse movements and the formation or development of *maria*. The Earth's orogenies are divided by periods of about 250 million years; a cycle of 1,000 million years seems appropriate for a smaller mass such as the Moon.

On this reckoning, the latest 'lunar orogeny' would correspond to the formation of *Mare Orientale*, perhaps contemporaneous to the bright-rayed craters. This may have happened some 500 million years ago. It must be appreciated that such an active period may itself continue for millions of years,[107] so that the temporary atmosphere is fed with further effusions, and, according to my calculations, should endure for 100 million years or so.[108]

5

The Iron Planet

The innermost Solar planet, Mercury has been named after the divine messenger of Olympus from the swiftness of its movements. Other things being equal, orbital velocities are inversely proportionàl to the square root of the distance from the Sun, which makes Mercury the quicksilver of the sky.

Though somewhat elusive in high northern latitudes because of its proximity to the Sun, Mercury averages the zero magnitude of Capella or Vega, rivals Sirius when brightest and shines clear in the morning or evening Mediterranean twilight, where it has been known since time immemorial.

Its mean distance from the Sun is 0.387AU or 57,910,000km, which corresponds to an orbital velocity of 47.87 km per sec. Mercury's orbit stands at an angle of 7° 17′ 3″ to the plane of the ecliptic, and is highly eccentric: it is more than one fifth 'out of the circle'. The Sun lies at one of the foci of the ellipse, which is 0.3075AU away at perihelion and 0.4667AU at aphelion. This difference works out as 23,816,320km and has manifold consequences, of which more later.

Mercury goes once round the Sun in 88 days (or 87,696, to be precise); it returns to the same position relatively to the Sun and the Earth—and so to the same phase—after a mean synodic period of 115.88 days. The combined eccentricities of the two orbits make this period vary considerably: Mercury's apparent distance from the Sun, or *elongation*, may be anything from 17° 50′ to 27° 5′. Even in the latter case Mercury is too close to the Sun for comfort; the 'air' around the Sun is agitated and observation difficult. Both Venus and Mercury, the two *interior planets*[109] moving within the Earth's orbit, are usually observed in daylight, except for the rare and brief treat of a total Solar eclipse.

This means that they are new when nearest and full—and more or less unobservable—when on the other side of the Sun, one of the reasons why our telescopic knowledge of these planets is scant and uncertain. To make up for that they can occasionally be seen in transit. The transits of Venus are very infrequent and occur in pairs, the last such in 1874 and 1882 and the next to come on 8 June 2004 and 5–6 June 2012. Mercury is more obliging; its transists recur after 7, 13 and 46 years. The last one, which I was unable to see owing to a thick overcast; was on 10 November 1973; but I did observe the planet crossing the Sun's disc on 7 November 1960 with an interesting result (p 92).[110]

A transit affords an opportunity to study the planet's atmosphere and dark side.

Mercury is the smallest terrestrial planet with a mean diameter of 4,878km.[111] At optimum viewing Mercury is some 150 million km distant, and its telescopic appearance is comparable to the Moon seen with the naked eye, with ill-defined bright and dark areas indicating rotation.[112]

The latter presented a thorny problem. The issue was complicated by strong librations (due to the high orbital eccentricity), amounting to 23° 42' each way in longitude plus an unknown libration in latitude arising from the axial tilt, which remains undetermined. Moreover, the Sun as seen from Mercury is far from being a geometrical point: it subtends an angle of 1° 10' at aphelion and 1° 44' at perihelion, and will always peep by half this amount round the geometrical terminator, producing a twilight effect.

With a less eccentric orbit, Solar body tides would have forced Mercury into a tied-up rotation. Yet both theory and radar echoes pointed to a direct axial period of 59 days, now refined to 58.65. The curious result is that Mercury turns once round relatively to the Sun in 176 terrestrial days—twice its orbital period—while the Sun at perihelion and aphelion always stands on one of the two alternative meridians. How-

ever, this cannot eliminate librations. Any libration in latitude
depends on the orbital position alone; our seasons are the result
of such a libration. Mercury's longitudinal wobble is affected
by the slow spin of the planet, but only slightly. The albedo of
Mercury is 0.06, so that it is even darker than the Moon (0.07).
The variation in brightness with phase and polarimetric
analyses also suggested a close resemblance between the two
bodies; but there was no firm knowledge of the true appearance
of Mercury before the *Mariner 10* television survey in 1974.[113]

Mariner 10

Mariner 10 is still intact at the time of writing (1976). It has
been equipped to study magnetic fields, the interaction of these
and of the target planets more generally with the Solar Wind;
for the 'charged particle telescope experiment' (to determine
the fluxes of charged particles in space and near the planets);
celestial mechanics and radio occultation experiments; ultra-
violet spectroscopy; infra-red radiometry; and, last but not
least, television work.

There are two TV cameras: a wide-angle and a narrow-angle
one, each frame consisting of 700 vidicon scan lines embodying
835 coded bits or *pixels*, to be assembled by computer into
photographic images.[114] Associated with the cameras is a
filter wheel with seven positions, making use of colour and
polarising filters.

This two-planet, Venus/Mercury, mission was launched from
Cape Kennedy on 2 November 1973 and obtained, for comparison, very good picture mosaics of the Earth and the Moon
on the way out. It also made space observations of the comet
Kohoutek, shedding new light on the nature and composition
of these mysterious bodies. On 5 February 1974 *Mariner* passed
within 5,800km of the cloud decks of Venus and, decelerated
by its gravitational pull, dropped to the orbit of Mercury,
flying by at 750km from its surface on 29 March. Both planets
were approached from the night side, which allowed *Mariner*
to study their magnetotails and other plasma effects. The

Plate 14 Viking 1 lander's camera eyes the stone-scattered surface of Mars. When the first colour pictures came through they caused surprise by showing rusty-red ground and a bright sky *(NASA)*

Plate 15 Jupiter, photographed by *Pioneer 10*, showing the Great Red Spot, zones, belts, cloud structures, convective cells in the south and the shadow of the satellite Io *(NASA)*

Plate 16 Looking down on Jupiter's north pole (roughly on the terminator). This view of the giant planet, taken by *Pioneer 11* on 3 December 1974, had never been seen before; from Earth we always see a 'full' Jupiter, with the entire hemisphere illuminated by the Sun. The picture suggests that Jupiter's polar regions are more placid than the turbulent equatorial areas *(NASA)*
Plate 17 Saturn with its ring system fully 'open', photographed with 100-inch telescope. The Cassini Division shows clearly, as do the Jupiter-like belts and zones on Saturn's globe *(Mount Wilson and Palomar Observatories)*

gravitational field of Mercury threw *Mariner* into an elliptical orbit which brought it back to within 50,000km of the planet on 21 September 1974, this time from the sunlit side, and again on 16 March 1975 to as close as 320km of its dark northern hemisphere. *Mariner 10* continues to orbit the Sun and return to Mercury every 176 days.

It is rather a pity that this interval corresponds to Mercury's Solar day the same hemisphere facing the Sun on each occasion. As we have seen, 176 days is also twice the orbital period of Mercury, so that *Mariner*'s successive approaches are unable to check on the planet's axial tilt, assumed at present, somewhat improbably, to be exactly 0°.

No great errors in mass and diameter have been found. *Mariner*'s evidence leaves the accepted values for Mercury's surface gravity (0.38g) and escape velocity (4.3km per sec) substantially unchanged, and for a diameter of 4,878km yields a mean density of 5.44.[115] This is less than the Earth's 5.52, but this is due chiefly to central gravitational compression, whose effect in the much smaller mass of Mercury will be comparatively slight. Thus Mercury must be made up of intrinsically heavier materials—not unexpected in a body condensed within the hot central part of the Solar nebula (p 20), deficient in the lighter elements.

Mercury should be rich in the heavy metals—lead, gold, the platinum group, tungsten, uranium, thorium, even mercury— and above all iron, the most abundant heavy metallic element in the universe. The symbol ♂ stands for Mars, the Roman God of War, for iron and the male sex—but it properly belongs to Mercury, the true Iron Planet.

S Plagemann has calculated that Mercury's nife core, having a mean density of 7.3, should account for 2,112km of its radius. Without attaching much weight to that 112km, this leaves less than 400km for sima, which fills nearly a half of the Earth's radius. Even on Earth the average thickness of sial is barely 10km, and sial should be substantially absent from Mercury. Diamonds may be comparatively common there but quartz will be a rarity; the surface rocks will be mainly basic and ultrabasic, which is borne out by the *Mariner* photography.

Mercury has an appreciable magnetic field and a magneto-sphere similar to that of the Earth in structure, with a bow shock on the Sunward side and a tail of deflected Solar Wind. The field strength at closest approach was measured at 90–100γ ($\gamma = 10^{-5}$ gauss), and may be about twice as strong at the surface. The corresponding Earth field is 30,000γ. Yet Mercury's weak magnetic field is sufficient to provide a noticeable screening effect on the Sun's corpuscular radiation at the Earth's distance, and this affects our weather to a statistically significant extent.

The data from the third flyby confirm that Mercury's magnetic field is indigenous to the planet, despite its slow rotation. This has been thought inadequate to generate the dynamo effect in the core[116] which is most certainly molten, at least over a part of its radius. Helium seems to be the prime constituent of Mercury's atmosphere, and as helium is the by-product of the decay of uranium and thorium[117] this indicates powerful sources of radiogenic heat.

No ionosphere has been detected in the occultation experiment, which is said to limit the possible ionospheric density to 100 electrons per cm^3 and ground-level barometric pressure to 0.01mb, but there may be an ionospheric layer, or layers, 100km above the surface. A Mercurian ionosphere would be comparatively low, being pinched by the strong Solar Wind. 'Flickering auroræ' and a weak luminosity were observed on Mercury's dark side, which is attributed to a thin atmosphere of helium, argon, neon, and possibly xenon (estimated at 10^{-11} of Earth's sea-level density). Other gases may be present. On the other hand, according to Herzberg and Kahn[118] the density must be at least 100 times more to produce those 'flickering auroræ'.

Beyond question, Mercury is poorly placed to retain an appreciable atmosphere for long. Nevertheless, its surface gravity exceeds that of Mars, and the situation is somewhat complicated.

For one thing, Mercury's days and nights are—librations apart—three terrestrial months long, and very hot and very cold respectively. The subsolar temperatures are put at 570°K (say, 300°C) at aphelion and 700°K (approx 430°C) at perihelion; but the mid-afternoon temperature measured by the IR radiometer aboard *Mariner 10* was only 460°K, dropping to 150°K when the instrument eye crossed the terminator and continuing to decline to 100°K (−173°C) at local midnight. A further drop before dawn may be assumed. The situation is substantially lunar. However, the surface day temperature will also decline rapidly away from the subsolar point, owing to the roughness of the ground and the shadows cast by it. Near the poles it will actually drop below freezing-point, so that it would be possible to land on Mercury in daytime without being crisped alive.

This means that all gases and vapours will be distilled away from the hottest to the coldest parts of the surface. There they will be largely precipitated or absorbed by the porous regolith, whose existence is inferred from the *Mariner* data. Thus a wide circle round the subsolar point would be more or less airless, which would apply (to a lesser degree) to the night hemisphere as well. Such atmosphere as exists will be found mainly near the poles and along the terminator especially the morning terminator, where the atmosphere would be released from the surface by evaporation and desorption.

Atmospheric density and composition may also vary with local degassing, as on the Moon (p 74), and volcanic activity. Furthermore, Mercury's orbit crosses the disc of Zodiacal Light round the Sun, which seems to consist mainly of dust, although some of its elements develop comet-like fantails. Anyway, Mercury could easily pick up a temporary halo of such material, which would later settle on its surface. Many substances which are solid on Earth (sulphur, stannic and ammonium chlorides and even common salt) could vaporise appreciably in the heat of Mercurian midday. All this is worth bearing in mind because many observations indicate a denser atmosphere; and although mistakes are made by observers,[119] their reports are often vindicated by later findings.

The lights on Mercury's night side are a case in point. These had often been seen during transits and dismissed as due to instrumental defects. Yet they were confirmed by *Mariner 10*, which entirely missed the otherwise well-authenticated 'Ashen Light' of Venus. They must have been pretty bright. Another transit phenomenon is a brilliant eccentric point of light on the dark disc of Mercury. This may be an image of the Sun, reflected on telescopic lenses—but no such effect has been seen during the transits of Venus, although there *are* reports of broad, bright or dark haloes similar to those observed round the disc of Mercury. These haloes can be sharp-edged or diffuse; are they illusory, or somehow connected with the magnetosphere of Mercury? What I saw on 7 November 1960 was something quite different: a thin bright-blue line round Mercury as it was crossing the darkened limb region of the Sun, and no other lights or haloes.[120] The observation was by projection on to white cardboard from a reflecting telescope in good seeing. A faint ring of light was also seen round Mercury

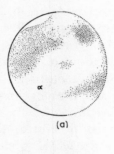

(a)

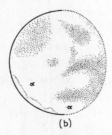

(b)

Fig 3 Atmospheric veils on Mercury, affecting the prominent figure-of-five marking (after E M Antoniadi, *Le Planète Mercure*)

off the disc of the Sun on several occasions, lastly by Futschek and Severinski with the 20-cm refractor of the Urania Observatory, Vienna.[121]

From polarimetric analysis Dollfus deduced an atmosphere with a ground pressure of about 1 millibar. Moroz in Russia found a strong μm IR absorption of CO_2, corresponding to a pressure of 3.3 millibars. Kozyrev observed the 1973 transit spectroscopically and found lines of hydrogen 25 seconds before the first contact with the Sun[122]—both Venus and Earth have hydrogen haloes, derived, it seems, from the Solar Wind. Finally, Antoniadi speaks of atmospheric veils 'much more frequent and obliterating than those of Mars'.[123] Was he deluded? He was a most experienced observer, working with the excellent 84-cm refractor at Meudon. True, *Mariner 10* has given no indication of anything of the kind; but a volcanic eruption or meteoritic impact could raise a cloud of gas and dust and cause a local obscuration.

Mercury's surface

During the first flyby *Mariner 10* took 2,850 pictures of Mercury from various distances—most of them of superb quality.[124] The resolution, which clearly depends on the distance, reaches about 300 metres at closest approach. The scale is comparable to that of the best Earth-based telescopic photographs of the Moon.[125] The second approach produced a further 2,000 photographs; and more good pictures, especially of the boulder-strewn area antipodal to Caloris, were obtained on 16 March 1975.[126]

Mercury's surface area measures 74,820,000 square km—about twice as much that of the Moon. But only one hemisphere was accessible at the three flybys, and not all of it at suitable viewing angles. As things are now, about 37 per cent of the entire surface has been covered with map-adequate accuracy. Although the experience of Mars and the Moon shows that it is unsafe to infer too much about an unknown hemisphere from the known one, there is no present reason to expect very great surprises on the other side of Mercury; many of the visible features obviously continue beyond the terminator, thus greatly reducing the area of uncertainty.

The general appearance vividly recalls the Moon. The colourings and albedoes are very similar; the former are very subdued, but comparison of the orange-filter and UV views reveals some local differences on the 50-km scale. Some features are bluer and others redder with no great consistency in relation to surface relief. The Mercurian crater Kuiper is nearly as bright as Aristarchus on the Moon, and the general albedoes of the cratered terrains are comparable. But B C Murray and others observe that 'the smooth plains of Mercury are significantly darker . . . Mercury's appearance is blander . . . Albedo boundaries between light and dark regions are less distinct on Mercury . . .'.[127]

Thermal (IR) and polarimetric data indicate a similar surface texture below the level of resolution. A regolith, similar to the Moon's, may be inferred. But to what extent this and the highland colouring is due to the meteoritic 'gardening' of country rocks, and to what is an external acquisition from the Zodiacal dust, remains undecided; it may be of some importance for the chemistry and structure of the Mercurian globe. Everything points to its being more basic than the Moon.

Mercury's craters are unevenly distributed, sparser and less rugged than the lunar, although some rings are densely bunched, like grapes. There are a few confluent 'beetle formations' rather like Hainzel or Palitsch on the Moon, occasionally with intersecting walls; these appear to shun the equatorial regions and concentrate near the poles. Lunar-type paired craters likewise occur; but overlaps are comparatively rare (possibly as a result of sparsity), and the lunar rule of the overlapping crater being smaller than the overlapped one seems to be largely honoured in the breach. Quite a few Mercurian craters have convex floors.

Murray and others describe formations over 200km in diameter as *basins*.[128] They find that the surface density of basins over 300km is only about half the lunar equivalent, and the ground so far studied shows none between 500 and 1,300km—

there are five such on the Moon. Measurements from a sample of 131 craters from 3–200km in diameter show that Mercurian craters are 'significantly shallower'. Many large rings are enclosed within a wider second ring which is roughly twice as large and lower. This structure is not unknown on the Moon, which casts some doubt on the suggestion that this is due to the impact being reflected from a discontinuity below the surface. Concentric cone sheets provide a more likely explanation. There are a few small, very dark areas which are probably ultrabasic, but these show no clear association with crater floors; and the walled plains, commonly lined with lunabase on the Moon and therefore darker, are on Mercury often *brighter* than their surroundings.

The bright areas of Mercury owe their existence mainly to rayed craters. Most rays seem to be of the Tychonic type (p 67) and may exceed 1,000km in length. But this resemblance may be somewhat superficial: some rays are very broad, curiously curved and not obviously connected with a crater. On the other hand, association with surface fractures is often unmistakeable. In other cases the ejected material looks quite thick, blanketing the intervening terrain and casting perceptible shadows. Small bright craterlets may mark recent meteoritic strikes. But there are also some bright hills, including conical cratered peaks recalling spatter cones, at the meeting of crater walls.

Mercury sports one large basin, Caloris, most of which lies beyond the terminator in the *Mariner* 'frames'. It is equatorially located and measures 1,300km across within an ill-defined mountain girdle. The mountains are of the Haemus-to-Apennine type but are low by lunar standards, and do not exceed 2km above the basin floor. They are pseudo-radial, but closer inspection reveals a system of grid lineaments, intersecting at right angles and traceable for some 2,000km beyond the Caloris basin. Indeed, this system is probably planet-wide and related to the Solar tides and librations in Mercury's highly eccentric orbit.

Caloris also falls about the perihelic meridian of Mercury,

which points to a similar origin. In any case it must have been subject to great tidal stresses, which goes some way to accounting for its structural features.

Caloris is rather larger than the Moon's Sea of Rains (1,200km), to which it bears some resemblance, as it also does to the smaller *Mare Orientale*. But the mountain girdles of these lunar *maria* are 3–4 times as high, and neither is as excessively fractured as Caloris. There are turtleback lava-fields on the Earth, the Moon and Mars, but this development seems to be substantially absent from Mercurian crater fillings. Yet the whole interior of Caloris is one continuous turtleback of fractures: some straight but mostly sinuous, with tholoidal ridges extruded from these, sometimes cracked along the top and/or passing over into gaping chasms. These fractures are up to 6km wide, and at least the widest ones are flat-bottomed.

The ridges average from $1\frac{1}{2}$–13km across, stand up to 300m high—like the lunar wrinkle-ridges which they closely resemble, especially away from the centre of Caloris. They are fairly short, however: not over 300km.[129] Sparsely scattered over the area are medium-sized, clear-cut bowl-shaped craters, clearly not impact-formed, and connected with the turtleback pattern. The highest-resolution elements of the photo-mosaic show the surface to be pitted with swarms of blowholes (rather like parts of the Moon's surface north of *Mare Frigoris*), suggesting melting by internal heat and pneumatolysis.

There is no striated ground about Caloris, such as is found about *Mare Orientale*. There are plenty of rift-valleys or 'gouges', but no graben-grooves (p 64), nor anything like the lunar sinuous rilles, or the river-beds of Mars (p 124)—at least in the known part of Mercury and at the present limit of resolution. Crater-chains and confluent crater-valleys are common. There are no visible signs of atmospheric erosion[130]— yet the subdued character of the large rings recalls Mars rather than the Moon, so that whatever Mercury's erosive agencies may be, they are more effective than those on the Moon.

What Murray calls 'plains material' and I call 'pancake terrain', covers most of the area within some 2,000km around the visible rim of Caloris, but is also found in the north polar lands and patchily elsewhere. It vividly recalls parts of the Moon's Ocean of Storms, with typical wrinkle-ridges, domed structures and lobate lava-fronts, which Murray and others suspect but profess not to see. Indeed, most of the Mercurian surface is 'semi-marial' rather than 'highland' in lunar terms. The ground between the craters is comparatively level, although often roughened or 'knurled'.

This type of surface grades over into what has been described as 'weird' or 'hilly and lineated terrain'. This is concentrated mainly in the area antipodal to Caloris, which has given rise to the idea that it represents a kind of echo of the great impact supposed to have excavated the *mare*. Yet, since it lies on the perihelic meridian, tidal forces and/or the intense heat of the Sun come to mind as possible causes.

Intensive heat erosion, or some form of frost shattering, may be one of these, and both require the presence of moisture. But sulphur, which is a likely volcanic material, has a high coefficient of thermal expansion. Melting day by day, it could work itself into the rock cracks and subsequently split these open. Sorption, or adsorption in depth, leads to the dilation of molecular lattices. It operates even at extremely low barometric pressures and increases steeply with falling temperature.[131] As the temperature rises again, the sorbed gas is given off and the sorbent contracts. Metals can be reduced to powder in this way, and porous, clinkery rocks should be similarly affected.

Be this as it may, this 'hilly and lineated terrain' is characterised by shallow dish-plains with poorly-developed or absent boundary heights, 50–100km in diameter, ensconced among a largely uncratered, moderately high ground which is broken up into short elongated ridges and hollows. It resembles the Martian chaotic terrain (p 124) in having a common base. Plate 11 is typical of such ground structure, and displays small rift valleys and sinuous channels, some branched, of unknown origin.

A peculiar feature of Mercury's landscape is lobate, wavy scarps up to 3km high and some hundreds of kilometres long.[132]

These appear to originate in overthrusts or reverse faults, arising from the shrinkage of the interior. The scarps lack any constant orientation and extend into the polar regions. But there are also some clearly meridional alignments and gentle ground swells, disregarding relief.

Since orbital velocities at Mercury's distance from the Sun are so much higher than at that of the Moon (let alone Mars), impact craters on Mercury should be larger and deeper in proportion—but the reverse is the case. I, for one, view references to primordial bombardment with suspicion; but it is nevertheless true that the cratered surface constitutes a geologically (or 'hermologically') ancient phase of development, followed by contraction and emplacement of the 'plains material'.

The evidence of tectonic and magmatic activity makes it a fair surmise that Mercury, too, has its orogenetic cycles, which seem largely to exhaust themselves in an increased flow of heat from the interior. Yet volcanic activity and gas exhalation may also be assumed.

Infra-red radiometry indicates small variations (of 2°C or so) in the surface temperature, but no 'hot spots' have been discovered at the scale of resolution of 10–50km. The rates of cooling bear witness to a thermal inertia slightly above the lunar—but this information must be regarded as provisional only.

Futute research may modify this verdict, but on the present showing Mercury is an unexciting world.

6

The improbable Venus

The Solar System has two pairs of planetary twins: Uranus and Neptune among the giants, and Earth and Venus among the dwarfs. In so far as a planetary endowment is defined by size and mass there is nothing much to choose between them, yet they are significantly different. I once described Earth and Venus as 'non-identical twins'.[133] It used to be thought that their differences may be more apparent than real. But in the words of Sherlock Holmes, 'Eliminate the impossible and what is left, however improbable, is the truth'. And it would be hard to imagine a more improbable planet than Venus.

Table II compares the indisputable basic data relating to the two planets. In combination with the orbital motion, the period of rotation obtained from radar echoes gives Venus a mean solar day, or *sol*, of 118 days and 8 hours. The inclination is given as 178°, or $-2°$, which means that Venus, like Uranus, is out of step with the other planets and turns backwards, from east to west—in a period longer than its year, withal. This is peculiar enough. But when the rotation is examined spectroscopically or from the movement of surface markings (mainly in UV), a retrograde axial period of only 4.1 days is obtained, which has been emphatically confirmed by the *Mariner 10* television survey.[134]

Moreover, the temperature charts of the surface of Venus and some other data suggest an inclination of 20–30°. The sol corresponding to the UV period is 3 days 22 hours and 20 minutes. The visible surface of Venus is all cloud, and it is possible that if our own day were determined from the movements of the cloud systems it would be nothing like the correct

TABLE II

	EARTH	VENUS
Mean distance from Sun	1AU (149.60 × 10⁶km)	0.723AU (108.21 × 10⁶km)
Orbital eccentricity	0.0167	0.0068
Orbital period	365.256 days	224.701 days
Diameter	12,576km	12,100km
Mass	1.000	0.815
Surface gravity	1g	0.903g
Escape velocity	11.18km per sec	10.36km per sec
Mean density	5.517	5.25
Polar inclination	23°27′	?
Sidereal axial period	23 hrs 56 mins 04 secs	?
Mean solar day	24 hrs 03 mins 56.55 secs	?
Mean flux of Solar energy at orbit	Solar Constant (2 gramme-cals per cm² per min)	1.9 Solar Constants
Visual bond albedo	0.36	0.76

24 hours. Still, the situation is extremely puzzling, to say the least.

It can be justifiably argued that, having been formed nearer the centre of the planetogenic cloud, Venus had from birth a composition somewhat different to that of the Earth. But since their mean distances from the centre of the Sun differ by only some 25 per cent, the initial differences in composition would be of the same order.

As we know, the mean density of a planet is partly a matter of internal compression due to gravity. The small difference in the radii of the two planets can be disregarded in the first approximation. The surface gravity of Ven.s is 0.9g, and the corresponding compressive force will be this much less. If we now multiply the Earth's mean density into 0.9 we get a putative mean of about 5.0 for Venus—*if* it has an identical inner structure, temperature and composition. But this is 0.25

short of the actual figure, despite our having taken a radius too large by over 200km. Density can vary abruptly under pressure through changes in crystalline habit; interior temperatures are another important factor,[135] so that all this is very rough reckoning. But it does bear out the initial suspicion that Venus contains a somewhat higher proportion of intrinsically heavier material than the Earth.

We would thus expect a larger nife core and a thinner sialic crust. The heavy nuclides uranium and thorium could also be more abundant on Venus. Their radioactive decay generates helium, which is present in the planet's atmosphere and so may be invoked in support of this surmise. If so, Venus may well be the hotter of the two bodies and the thermal gradients in its crust could be steeper; a very lively vulcanism may be expected.

It will be recalled (p 13) that the internal heat of the Earth leaks out at the surface at the average rate of 0.000072gram-cals/cm² per minute, so that the contribution of the Earth's own heat to its surface climate is barely 0.00001 of the Solar Constant. If now the leakage on Venus were 100 times as much, which seems very unlikely, it would only amount to one thousandth of the Solar Constant and could not have any great effect on the planet's climate. But this is not quite the whole story, and I will return to it later on.

Certain highly speculative assumptions about the origin of the Solar System would make Venus deficient in water and sulphur.[136] But water vapour has been recorded spectroscopically in the atmosphere of Venus and by the Russian *Venera* probes within the atmosphere itself. And it is currently forgotten that the clouds of Venus give a reflection curve that fits very neatly that of a cloud of water-ice crystals produced in a laboratory (Fig 9).[137] Sulphuric acid has been found in the upper atmosphere,[138] and it is even suggested that the top layer of Venusian clouds consists of droplets of concentrated sulphuric acid. Whether this is true or not, sulphuric acid is a common volcanic and industrial pollutant formed by the interaction of sulphur dioxide with water; and its presence does not bear out the hypothetical shortage of sulphur and water.

Sulphuric acid is also present in the Earth's atmosphere, but on Venus there seems to be about four times as much of it.[139]

Two other highly corrosive substances—hydrochloric acid (HCl) and hydrofluoric acid (HF)—have been identified by interferometric spectroscopy but their concentrations are minute: one part per million and per 100 million respectively.[140]

Put together, all this seems to bear witness to lively volcanic activity.

Smaller in mass and closer to the Sun, Venus would normally be expected to have retained a somewhat thinner atmosphere than the Earth. When seen as a narrow crescent, both planets show a similar prolongation of the cusps due to atmospheric refraction. When the Sun is behind Venus (at inferior conjunction or at transit) its dark disc is outlined by the so-called 'silver thread' of light—and so is the Earth during a solar eclipse viewed from space or the Moon. The effects are closely comparable, though the ring round Venus may be taken to extend no farther down than its thick cloud banks. Yet Earth has its clouds, too; the silver thread of Venus is often knotted; isolated clouds have been observed during transits, and a clear break during the 1874 transit.[141] So there are a few holes in that blanket, even though none such were found by *Mariner 10*!

Our present knowledge of the planet is derived primarily from *Mariner 10* and the Russian *Veneras 9* and *10*. These probes have dispelled some misconceptions about it, without, however, providing any final solution of its mysteries. Nevertheless, the earlier telescopic observations have not lost all their relevance.

Venus observed

Breaks in the Venusian clouds are comparatively rare and fleeting and the overcast is substantially complete. This makes the face of the planet in the telescope singularly featureless, especially when observed against a dark sky in the evening or morning, close to the twilight arc, where the air is agitated and the seeing is poor. But there is no special difficulty about observing Venus high up in the sky, at or near the local meridian, in full daylight. It is a very bright object, and it helps to have the contrast muted.

In daytime, with steadier air, a practised eye will generally discern a few faint shadings. These usually take the form of three dark bays extending from the terminator into the bright part of the disc, and occasionally crossing it in belts. The markings are brownish, like the belts of Jupiter but much fainter. They are enhanced by the use of filters, becoming progressively stronger towards the violet end of the spectrum, and have often been photographed in blue, violet and UV.[142]

Colour vision is determined by the combined response of three kinds of receptors in the retina, with peak sensitivities in red, green and blue; all colours arise from the various combinations of these three primaries. Colour separation filters approximate to the same arrangement, but the colour is obtained by default. Thus a red filter suppresses the green and blue elements and shows them dark, and so on. In this way a true colouring can be distinguished from an illusory one.

The disc of Venus is tinted with a touch of creamy or lemon yellow, but its colour index is exactly the same as that of the Sun. This is our standard of whiteness, so that to all intents and purposes Venus is snow-white. An ochre tone may line the terminator, as it does on Earth.

On 19 June 1780 Sir William Herschel saw a 'bluish, darkish spot' on Venus, and bluish spots were reported on various occasions between 1895 and 1930 by Jarry-Deloges, Molesworth and MacEwen.[148] These may be interpreted as gaps in the clouds, similar to the wide gap recorded at the 1874 transit. The clouds themselves have been observed by Kuiper, Dollfus, Lenham and Focas to break up into bright dots under high magnification in good seeing.[144] I have not seen any such effects myself, but in using filters I have often found that when darker areas appeared in red they did not necessarily coincide with those seen in green and blue. Furthermore, near the cusps, the red-filter and blue-filter markings seemed to alternate in a period of about eight days, which may deserve investigation.[145]

Not all markings of Venus are dark. Bright areas, usually more or less circular, also occur and may cause a deformation of the terminator. The 'polar caps' are a special class of such markings: they look very much like those of Mars and never stray far from the cusps, although they need not coincide with these. They are not always visible and vary in brilliance and clearness of outline. They are best seen through a green filter, becoming diffuse in blue and violet. Very rarely such a 'cap', usually in the south, is so bright that it can be made out easily without filters. Occasionally the cap is accompanied by one or more brilliant star-points, once interpreted as snow-clad mountains rising above the clouds.

Over a period of time the 'caps' and the shadings disclose a belted arrangement. In 1954 G P Kuiper at McDonald plotted a long series of violet-filter photographs on to a white globe. He assumed that the belts would run parallel to the equator, and thus sought to determine the position of the poles of Venus. This resulted in an inclination of about 32°. As already mentioned, ultra-violet photography in France and the USA revealed a systematic movement of the dark markings, yielding a retrograde axial period of 4 days or so. B Guinot,[146] using interferometric spectroscopy (no longer limited to the UV) with the 118-cm reflector at Le Houga (France), obtained a similar result.

A well-known visual feature is the 'Ashen Light'. When

RED   GREEN   BLUE

Fig 4 Progressive aspects of Venus, observed by the author through a tricolour separation set of filters. Compare the blue view with Plate 5

Venus is in crescent phase the dark part of the disc can some-times be seen faintly illuminated, rather like 'the new moon in the old moon's arms'. It is best seen if the bright crescent is blocked out by an occulting bar. Early in the nineteenth century the German astronomer Paula von Gruithuisen suggested that this was due to the illuminations to celebrate the accession of a new 'Emperor of Venus'. These emperors must be very short-lived, as the Ashen Light can at times be seen on several occasions in a single month. It is not always uniform, and may have a spotty or patchy appearance. Wavy lines may also appear within it. Owing to spherical perspective it may be intensified towards the limb into what I have called the 'woollen thread'. Sometimes the light brightens up towards the cusps, suggesting polar aurorae.

There can be no doubt that the true origin of the Ashen Light is electric. It is a night-sky glow, similar to that in our own sky but estimated to be 50–80 times stronger (Gordon Newkirk, N A Kozyrev).[147] It has a line emission spectrum sufficiently strong to be photographed, and Brian Warner[148] found in 1960 a good fit between many of the lines and those of neutral, singly- and doubly-ionised oxygen. This had a cool reception, but we shall see presently that his finding is supported by *Mariner 10*.

On 8 October 1959 I observed a bright point of light on the dark limb of Venus, some 30° from the southern cusp. The planet was a crescent about halfway between half and new. Similar 'flares' have been seen on Mars (p 138), but I have no other report of a flare on Venus.

Fig 5 shows a temperature chart of Venus, based on its radiation in the infra-red. It relates to the top layer of the atmosphere, which is very cold, between about -90 and $-60°C$. The measurements of planetary heat in the 'water window' by W M Sinton and J R Strong put the temperature of the cloud tops at $234°K$ ($-39°C$), which is close to the expected 'greysphere temperature' of $228.8°K$. No significant difference between the bright and dark half of the planet has been found. The infra-red radiation cannot cross the clouds

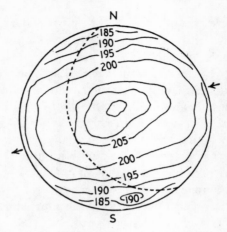

Fig 5 Infra-red temperature chart of Venus, after Murray and Wildey. Isotherms are at intervals of 5° K

(which shows that these provide a perfect trap for it). But the longer microwave radio emissions are unobstructed by an electrically neutral atmosphere: they can, in fact, pass through solid rock. When Venus was observed at between 3 and 21cm the corresponding 'brightness temperature' increased steadily with the wavelength to between 600 and 800°K.[149] This would indicate that the surface was very hot. The brightness temperature, however, is not wholly inequivocal: it is calculated on the assumption that its origin is wholly thermal and the radiator behaves as a perfectly black body. Various electrical processes can generate similar emission without heat. This gave rise to a lively controversy.[150]

The *Mariner* flybys

NASA has despatched three flyby *Mariner* missions to Venus, numbered *2* and *5* in 1962 and 1967 respectively, and *10* in 1973. The latter was intended primarily for the study of Mercury (p 88), but the spacecraft approached the dark side of Venus on 5 February 1974 and passed within 5,785km of its cloud decks.

Unlike the earlier probes, *Mariner 10* carried TV equipment with a set of filters. (Unfortunately, no green filter was included: this might have tested the reality and nature of the regular 'polar caps'.) The orange views of the planet are predictably blank (except at the limb, where they reveal three uniform layers of haze, some 6km thick, enveloping the whole globe). But there is a wealth of detail in the UV exposures (Plate 5): belted cloud structure, convection cells indicating ascending and descending air currents, cirrus clouds, bright caps and dark collars in the polar regions. The cloud movements confirm the 4-day period, which declines to two days towards the poles. The latter is clearly due to the equatorial air preserving its original velocity on a declining perimeter as it spirals up to the poles.

Yet, on the present views, the situation is incomprehensible.

Richard Goody may well speak of a 'toroidal wind',[152] but this explains nothing. Such a pattern of circulation clearly requires the equatorial air to be very much warmer than the polar. Yet if the Sun takes 118 days to move round the equator to an observer on Venus, how could such an equatorial excess of heat and a 'toroidal wind' originate? Solar heat would obviously build up at the subsolar point, whence the air would stream away to all sides in a star-pattern. A tendency to this type of circulation is present and manifests itself in the so-called 'Y effect'. A kind of 'eye' forms at the subsolar point and the weather belts are prised apart round it, but later resume their parallel alignment. This, though, is just what one would expect from a four-day period and the latter is a fact—at least the upper atmosphere revolves in this cycle. But there is no reasonable explanation why it should be turning 60 times faster than the solid ball of Venus at the equator and more than 100 times faster than it at high latitudes: this just does not make sense. To make matters worse, Fig 5 shows a temperature difference between the equator and the poles of not more than 30°C, and microwave temperatures are substantially uniform all over the globe. Now only a steep temperature gradient could drive winds of such ferocity, and no engine will work unless there is a transfer of energy from one of its parts to another.

On a rapidly spinning planet which is cold at the poles and warm in the tropics, tropical air will tend to flow towards the poles and be deflected in the sense of rotation on the way, and conversely in the case of the polar air stream. This is the origin of Earth's westerlies and easterlies, and of weather belts. But Venus is supposed to turn round in 243 days and 8 hours—a period longer than its year—so that this explanation does not fit. The further difference is that the atmosphere of the planet is about 100 times as massive as ours, so that whereas our winds blow close to the ground, the seat of the atmospheric circulation observed in the ultra-violet is high above the lower clouds. Somewhere lower down there must be an oppositely directed flow of polar air, with a shearing force between the two forming whirlpools similar to our cyclones and anti-cyclones. Those bright circular areas occasionally seen in the telescope may be their outward manifestation.

And in fact *Mariner 5*'s radio occultation experiment did find that the atmosphere has a two-tiered structure, with a marked discontinuity at an estimated altitude of 30–40km.[152] The results of the *Mariner 10* occultation are more specific: they reveal 'four distinct temperature inversions', at altitudes put at 56, 58, 61 and 63km. Its X-band signal, corresponding to 3.56cm, was absorbed in the clouds, but the 13-cm S-band crossed this barrier.[153] Because of this, however, microwaves cannot be relied on to reach the surface, and the radiation they represent need not originate there.

One of the *Mariner 10* 'frames' shows a strip of light detached from the cusp of the narrow crescent of Venus (which, it will be recalled, was approached from the night side). There is no sign of the Ashen Light—but, as the report states, 'there is evidence for intense air-glow at wave-lengths longward of 1,350 angstroms', the nature of which is 'unclear'. This radiation is extensive on both the night and day hemisphere. *Mariner 10*'s UV spectrometer has positively identified the emission of oxygen in this air-glow—an emission about ten times stronger than on Mars. Helium and hydrogen are also present in the outer atmospheric halo.

The ionosphere of Venus is comparatively cool (only some 580°K) and the rate of escape of hydrogen from Venus is roughly a tenth of that from the Earth. This ought to dispose of the idea that Venus has lost its water through photo-dissociation—the hydrogen having escaped to space and the oxygen been consumed in reactions with the ground (which is some 60km below in any case). Moreover, ozone is formed by the action of UV wavelengths of oxygen; it exists in the atmosphere of Mars; on Venus there is more oxygen and the Solar flux is about four times stronger, so there should be more ozone as well. One millionth of a per cent of ozone in our atmosphere is enough to prevent the penetration of short wavelengths and stop the photo-dissociation of water. Carbon dioxide is also subject to photo-dissociation in which free oxygen is generated. Thus on any reckoning this process should be equally effective on Venus, and the water content of its lower atmosphere be shielded against destruction. I will have more to say about that in connection with the Russian *Veneras*.

The magnetic field of Venus

Venus has an ionosphere with a density (10^4–10^5 electrons per cm^3) about a quarter of the Earth's.[154] This deflects the Solar Wind, with a bow shock and a comet-like magnetic tail 5 million km long. But *Mariner 10*'s measurements indicate that the external magnetic field of Venus is no more than one-twentieth of a per cent of the Earth's field. This is attributable to the slow rotation of Venus; the Earth's magnetism is generated by the dynamo effect of the conductive liquid core in relatively rapid rotation. Yet Mercury is also a slow spinner and although it has a much smaller mass it has a measurable magnetic field. Moreover, the upper atmosphere of Venus (which must be partly ionised) rotates quite fast, so that it too must act like a dynamo.

So far the field of Venus has been examined only close to the equatorial plane, and not near the poles. Mars was also found to be non-magnetic by such measurements, but readings taken closer to its surface do seem to reveal an appreciable magnetic field. This would be even more pertinent in the case of Venus, whose field must be expected to be pinched by the Solar Wind.

It all hinges on the reality of the 243-day radar period.

Suppose that the solid ball of Venus revolves at the rate comparable to the UV period. In this case the planet would be expected to have an appreciable magnetism, though no doubt weaker than that of the Earth. The Venusian counterpart of Earth's Van Allen belts would be forced down into the upper atmosphere, which would contain a belt of free electrons forming a current round the magnetic equator. On a well-known principle such a current would flow counter to the revolution of the planetary magnet, while being partly entrained by the atmosphere; it would also produce a radar echo very like the echo expected from the solid surface. This echo might be comparatively weak, but so too would the Doppler dispersion of velocites at the approaching and receding limbs, so that the peaks on the two sides of the 'bowl' profile would still be quite high.

This would be the source of the 243-day period, and it is well known that the magnetic and geographical axes need not coincide. There would, of course, be an echo from the surface as well. But here the dispersion of the Doppler shifts would be 60 or more times as great, and the maxima would be correspondingly low and so far out in the wings of the graph as to escape notice. In fact, some early Russian radar observations (1961) refer to a 'wide-band component' in the echo,[155] which may correspond to the reflection from the surface. This was discounted—but so were the 4-day UV period, the belts, the caps, and hosts of other observations which have subsequently proved significant.

In addition, such a revolving belt would generate a field of opposite polarity, which could largely cancel out the solid planet's own field. The three exposures of Plate 5 suggest an atmospheric belt unaffected by the general cloud movements. Radar echoes from Venus mapped at the Goldstone Tracking Station in California also have a somewhat peculiar appearance.

The general view contains a large number of clearly defined dark and bright areas, many of them circular and interpreted as craters. But the distribution of these features on either side of the 'radar equator' is almost a mirror image of the other side, and it is a little difficult to credit that any planetary surface could have such a configuration. As mentioned (p 108), there is no guarantee that radar reaches the surface, and the resulting pictures may be spurious.

However, the 1,000-foot fixed radio telescope at Arecibo, Porto Rico, has been refitted, and is claimed to be 500 times as sensitive for radar studies as any existing telescope of this type (the Russians are building a still larger one, but it is not in commission yet). Its programme includes a detailed mapping of Venus with a resolution of about 1 mile (say, 1.5km), accord-to Director F D Drake.[156]

The study of Venus abounds in contradictions. As the JPL *Status Bulletin No 19* has put it, 'The final results (from *Mariner 10*) are going to be basically new inputs to our understanding of Venus—her body and her clothing . . . Her clothes? —anybody with that much on must have a lot to hide.' *Veneras 9* and *10* have penetrated below 'the clothes' with some very interesting results—although these are far from conclusive and are again, at least in part, out of tune with the expectations. Unfortunately the landing modules survived only for about an hour, so that they could shed no light on the true period of rotation of the solid ball of the planet.

The *Veneras*

Since 12 November 1965 there have been ten Russian *Veneras*, or Venus probes. No 2 passed the planet; No 3 hit it; Nos 4, 5 and 6 entered the atmosphere and made some observations within it, but were put out of action by the intense heat and pressure before reaching the surface. But Nos 7 and 8 are said to have landed in operational order close to the equator, on the day and the night half respectively. Their results are consistent within themselves, and we may take up the story on

22 July 1972, when *Venera 8* is stated to have touched down and recorded a temperature of 470°C and a pressure of 90kg/cm².

The landing modules of *Veneras 9* and *10* had been redesigned to withstand high temperatures and pressures; the data were not radioed direct to Earth, but via orbiter craft which are still circling Venus at the time of writing (1976). No full report has been published yet. Unlike the earlier versions, these modules carried TV equipment and obtained clear, close-up panoramas (Plate 6).

These are remarkable because the illumination of the surface was expected to be very dim, only 2 per cent of the sunlight filtering through to the ground.[157] Yet both views show clear shadows directed towards the probe, so they could not have originated in any source of light carried by it. The horizon (which is some 200–300 metres distant) is convex, not concave as a result of the anticipated super-refraction, and the sky is bright. Indeed, according to Arnold Selivanov, one of the designers of the telemetric systems for spacecraft, 'it is as light on Venus at noon as it is on a cloudy day in Moscow in June.' The surface is rock-strewn, not sandy or dusty, and the two fish-eye views recall submarine photographs—which is perhaps not too surprising if it is remembered that the density of the Venusian air near the surface will be about a tenth that of water.

But the submarine analogy goes deeper than that.

Launched on 14 June 1975, *Venera 9* soft-landed its surface module on 21 October, on what appears to be the summit of a volcanic mountain about 2,500 metres above the reference zero level (how this has been determined has not been explained). It recorded a temperature of 738°K (465°C) and a barometric pressure of 85 atmospheres,[158] and remained operational for 53 minutes. The landscape shows boulders (described as 30–40cm in diameter) of geologically young appearance, many with sharp uneroded edges, and the intersticial ground is plausibly described as weathered rock fragments.

The *Venera 10* module touched down on 25 October 1975, some 2,200km away from the first landing site, in what has been described as a plain. It recorded a temperature of 728°K (455°C), a pressure of 91 atmospheres, and an appreciable wind of 3.5 metres per second,[159] and continued sending signals for 65 minutes. The rocks in the local panorama are different. They form large pancakes, often fractured, with both edges and fractures still sharp and angular. The Soviet commentator Dmitry Grigoriev remarked that they 'closely resemble the fractures of lamellar sedimentary rock or shales.' But the British TV commentator Professor G Watson thought they recalled submarine pillow lavas—rocks of very similar appearance do occur on Anglesey, North Wales. In the latter case the dark matter between the rocks is vegetation; and it *looks* very like the dark matter in the *Venera 10* picture.

The latter is not so clear as the *Venera 9* panorama, but at least one rock has a dark pattern that on Earth would be interpreted as a growth of lichen. Is it? At first sight this appears impossible, but a high-temperature biology that would be viable on Venus is chemically conceivable.[160] It could, for instance, be based on sulphuric acid (which is present on Venus) as the organic solvent. Of course this is speculation, and speculation is a dirty word in professional circles—but many of the hypotheses that have been given an official accolade are even less well founded.

The disappointing thing about the *Venera* pictures is that they show isolated areas of the surface not more than 600 metres in diameter with none of the approach views that would help us relate them to the general topography. In this they fall far short of the American lunar *Rangers* which, though destroyed on impact, did supply a series of consecutive pictures on the way to the target. Remembering that Venus is an Earth-sized planet, such small areas cannot be representative of the whole. In particular, conditions near the poles may be expected to be significantly different.

The *Veneras* are also said to have sampled the Venusian

atmosphere during their 75-minute descent from an altitude of 60km above the surface, and to have made measurements of sunlight, the atmosphere, clouds and soil.[161]

Atmosphere and climate

The *Novosti Bulletin No 26488* gives the following composition of the atmosphere as determined by *Veneras 9* and *10*: CO_2, approx 97 per cent; N_2, 2 per cent; O_2, 1 per cent and H_2O vapour, approx 1 per cent 'around the clouds'. The latter extend from an altitude of 30–35km for 30–40km and are suspected to consist of several layers, with the uppermost made up of droplets of a concentrated aqueous solution of sulphuric acid. It is further stated that atmospheric conditions at 50–55km are almost identical with those on Earth, which must presumably refer to temperature and pressure.

The volume composition of Earth's *dry* air is: N_2 78.09 per cent, O_2 20.95 per cent, CO_2 0.03 per cent and H_2O vapour variable (mainly near the ground), the mean being 0.1 per cent.

Superficially the two sets of figures look very different. But if we consider the CO_2 bound in Earth's limestone rocks, mineral coal and dissolved in the oceans the *total* amounts are comparable, although free CO_2 occurs in the atmosphere only as a trace constituent at the present time. If we further put the average ground-level barometric pressure on Venus at 90 atmospheres, and take into account the reduced surface gravity of 0.9 per cent, this will give us an atmosphere of 100 air masses (p 37). In terms of Earth's atmospheric proportions, this means that 2 per cent of N_2 on Venus amounts to 200 per cent on Earth, 0.1 per cent of O_2 to 10 per cent and 1 per cent of H_2O to 100 per cent.

Now the proportion of water vapour that air can contain without precipitation depends on its temperature and pressure, which control the saturation point. For instance, the mean temperature of the Earth's surface is $+14°C$, and at this temperature the vapour pressure of water is 12 torr (mmHg), which for the sea-level pressure of 760 torr makes 1.6 per cent of uncondensed vapour. The saturation point rises with temperature and drops with increasing pressure. At the cloud level of Venus the air temperatures are low and the barometric pressures are comparable to the terrestrial. It therefore follows that at this level the atmosphere of Venus contains 1,000 times as much water vapour as does that of the Earth. This is not really possible: condensation will occur before such a proportion could be reached, producing copious clouds composed of liquid droplets or ice crystals, according to their temperature. It would seem that ·it was these clouds that the *Veneras* have sampled.

But the air temperature increases downwards (by an average of 6.5°C per km on Earth, and by some 4.5°C per km for an atmosphere of pure CO_2); and as the temperature rises towards the planet's surface the saturation point will go up as well. Thus the lower atmosphere must contain a high proportion of water vapour to sustain the concentration measured at the cloud level. Moreover, the critical temperature of water is +374°C and the corresponding critical pressure is 217.7 atmospheres. Once the temperature exceeds the critical the vapour becomes a true gas and can no longer be condensed by pressure alone. This means that the limit imposed by the saturation point no longer applies, which will be the case with ground temperatures of 450°C or more. The atmosphere at ground level could be pure superheated steam.

We would thus have a kind of 'sea of superheated steam'—hellish indeed!—with 0.1 the density of water, which could turn to liquid as soon as the temperature and pressure permit. Under the pressure of 90 atmospheres water boils at 300°C or thereabouts. If, therefore, the temperatures at the poles of Venus are 150°C or so lower than at the equator, a real sea could form there. Moreover, such a sea would contain a high proportion of solutes (salts, etc), which would further raise its boiling-point.

It is often held that Venus has an isothermal lower atmosphere, with the same temperature everywhere, But in an isothermal atmosphere there can be no winds, for a wind requires a thermal gradient; and *Venera 10* recorded a wind of about 12km per second, or 7½mph. This may not sound like a great deal; but the force of a current depends not only on its speed, but also on its mass, and the density of air is one-tenth that of water. Such a current would be strong enough to knock down a tall building, and requires a corresponding 'engine' in the form of a temperature gradient to drive it. In any event this disposes of the idea that the bottom atmosphere is isothermal, and cold regions near the poles may be expected.

The high surface temperature of Venus is usually explained by the 'greenhouse effect' of CO_2. This is a handy phrase but of somewhat doubtful validity: Earth's seas are not boiling hot, despite the total greenhouse effect of water and average sunlight stronger than at the ground level of Venus. Nor is it at all clear how such a condition could have become established.

We may have to consider the possibility that present conditions have arisen through the build-up not of trapped solar radiation, but of the internal heat of Venus. Possibly, under the cover of a thermally-insulating atmosphere, the heat seeping out of the planet's interior has been continuously raising the temperature of the surface rocks (p 101) up to the present level. Alternatively there may have been vast outpourings of basaltic lavas, comparable to and perhaps exceeding those of Earth's Thulean Basalts. Lavas cool very slowly, and in this case could have passed their heat on to the atmosphere of carbon dioxide and water vapour (which are both excellent thermal traps) until the seas of Venus literally boiled off. The sources of internal heat could even be localised—we do not know enough to dismiss this possibility. And, after all, it may prove that there has been some error in the measurements and the conditions are less extreme than believed at present.

We may learn more about all that in December 1978*.[162] NASA is planning to send two *Pioneer* vehicles to Venus in the May and August of that year. As in the case of the *Veneras* and *Vikings* each space ship will include an orbiter weighing 1,100lb. This is to become a satellite of Venus, orbiting at an angle of

* Written in May, 1976.

60–70° with the equator, and having a close point (pariapsis) 200km and a far point (apoapsis) 60,000km from the surface. The orbiter will be designed to last for one Venusian year of 225 days and to make independent observations; but its main task will be to monitor the reports of the 'probe bus' (weighing between 841 and 1,800lb, and its probes: one large and three small).

The large probe will be equipped with a complex instrumentation for the study of the atmosphere and clouds: IR radiometers, altitude radar, meteorological apparatus, and (in the light of the Russian experience) no doubt TV cameras to give a wider visual coverage of the surface. It is to weigh 600lb and be protected by a heat shield.

The 'bus' itself will enter the atmosphere at about 130km above the surface and transmit information to the orbiter until burned out. It will release the large probe at about 70km and three small probes (160lb each) to ensure as wide a coverage of the atmosphere as possible. The highly-inclined orbit is meant to include sub-polar latitudes in the programme. The probes are to be equipped with parachutes, opening at an altitude of 40km. The present plans do not include a soft landing, but they are subject to modification.

'Seeding' the clouds of Venus?

To wind up, it has been suggested by Carl Sagan that while life on the surface of Venus appears impossible, its dense atmosphere may yet harbour some kind of aerial plankton. A project has also been mooted whereby the clouds of Venus would be seeded with unicellular algae, which would become such a plankton and multiply rapidly in the abundant carbon dioxide. This, it is claimed would be converted to oxygen and organic substances, thus modifying the atmospheric composition and eliminating the super-greenhouse effect. It would bring down the temperature and could make Venus habitable in a period short not only by geological but even by historical standards. All that can be said is that interference with nature on such a scale may have unpredictable results.

7

Mars: a 'little Earth?'

In size and mass Mars fits in about halfway between the Moon and the Earth, and it has some features in common with both.

Orbiting the Sun outside the Earth, Mars presents to the telescope a more-or-less full face, which is shadowless and gives it a deceptively smooth appearance. The orange, yellowish or pinkish background of the disc is blotched and belted with variable dark areas, which look greenish, bluish or purplish, and have been called *maria* by analogy with the Moon; but they are mere albedo or colour features and no longer figure on the modern relief maps. Their colouring has been the subject of some controversy which is not quite resolved yet; but although partly a contrast effect, it has been shown to be faint but real by filter analysis (see p 103). *Mariner 9* could shed no light on this problem, as its wide-angle camera filter wheel became stuck on orange early in the mission, while the narrow-angle camera worked with a yellow filter. The Russian *Mars 5* (1974) is said to have obtained some views of Mars through different filters, but these do not appear to have been published. The dark areas of Mars look purple in the approach colour photographs taken by the *Viking* orbiters, but this is somewhat suspect. Colour photography is often highly misleading; in some views of the Moon taken from space it has a deep-green or blue colour!

In any event, telescopic study revealed clouds, mists and hazes amply confirmed since, and seasonal changes in the intensity and colour of the *maria* related to the waxing and waning of the bright polar caps. These changes were interpreted as the growth and decay of vegetation, depending on the release of moisture from the snow-caps on the arid globe. Together with the rotational similarities (of which more shortly) this earned Mars the nickname of 'the little Earth'. The 'discovery' of the famous 'canals', alleged to form a geometrical network of spidery lines, following the great circles of the planet and interconnecting the *maria* (Schiaparelli, Lowell), gave rise to speculation about an advanced Martian civilisation. The reality of these features was hotly disputed. But polarimetric analysis (notably by Audoin Dollfus in France) indicated a ground-level barometric pressure of some 90mb which, though low, was shown to be adequate to sustain some terrestrial organisms.[163]

Thus a view had become established that Mars was, in Percival Lowell's phrase, 'an abode of life'.[164]

This picture was rudely shattered by the first close-ups of the planet, obtained in 1964 by the American flyby probe *Mariner 4*. These revealed a heavily cratered world, seemingly as lifeless as the Moon, while the simultaneous S-band occultation experiment reduced the expected atmospheric pressure by a factor of about ten. Mars emerged as a 'large Moon' rather than a 'little Earth'. Subsequent space research, however, has brought some startling revelations, and, although it found no 'canals', marked a steady retreat from this position, which has not run its full course yet.

Be that as it may, the 'vital statistics' of Mars are now known with considerable accuracy.

According to the latest measurements the Martian globe is strongly flattened at the poles, the equatorial and polar diameters being 6,786.8 and 6,751.6km respectively. The equator is inclined to the orbital plane at 25° 12', which compares to the Earth's 23° 27'. Since Mars revolves once in 24 hours 37 minutes and 22.67 seconds, this gives it an almost identical progression of nights and days with very similar seasons and climatic zones.[165]

The Martian year, however, is 686.98 terrestrial days long. Moreover, the orbit of Mars has a large eccentricity of 0.0934, so that it comes within 206,402,000km of the Sun at perihelion and withdraws from it to 248,745,000km at aphelion (mean distance 1.524AU, or 227.94 × 10^6km), with a corresponding variation in orbital velocity and the allowance of Solar heat and light. The latter ranges from 0.36 to 0.52 Solar Constants, averaging 0.43. This considerably affects the length and relative warmth of the seasons, which occur in reverse in the two hemispheres.

The southern spring and the northern autumn fall within the periphelic quarter of the orbit, measure 146 terrestrial days each, and are absolutely the shortest and relatively the warmest seasons. The aphelic northern spring and southern autumn see the smallest and coldest Sun for 199 days, while the 160-day southern summer and northern winter are absolutely the warmest and the coldest time on Mars respectively. But because of the precession of the equinoxes with a period of 51,000 years, this situation is reversed every half-cycle, which may have important climatic consequences.

Taking the Earth as the unit of reference, the mass of Mars is 0.1074 and the surface gravity 0.3799, or roughly $\frac{2}{5}g$. The behaviour of orbital craft indicates that the gravitational field of Mars is 'rougher' than that of either the Moon or the Earth, with at least three mascons (p 74) as well as comparable local defects of mass. This would indicate a slowness of isostasic adjustment and a relatively thick, mechanically strong crust.[166]

The mean density of 3.94 is nearer that of the Moon than of the Earth. Nothing is yet known about the internal constitution of the Martian globe, but there is ample evidence of recent and impressive vulcanism, as well as tectonic movements, and in the light of the seismic findings on the Moon a molten core must be expected. It has been proposed that this core is larger than the Earth's, but that instead of nife it is made up wholly or predominantly of troilite (FeS), a nonmagnetic sulphide of iron, which has an uncompressed density of about 4.6 and is known mainly from meteorites. This is meant to account for the relatively low mean density and the lack of a magnetic field. But the recent measurements by the

Russian probes *Mars 5* and *6* seem to show that Mars has an appreciable magnetism of its own, after all. The same theory, incidentally, assigns to Mars a larger proportion of water than to Earth.

There may be something in all this, but it is not unfair to suspect that the subsurface layer of Mars resembles that of the Moon and, except for the mascon areas, is honeycombed with caves.

Martian volcanic structures suggest basic lavas, but the comparatively high albedo of 0.16 indicates lighter, more silicic rocks, and this has been confirmed by spectra obtained by *Mariner 9* during the great 1971 dust storm (*see below*). The 'dust' seems to be like terrestrial loess, which is a fine rock-flour of glacial origin composed of clayey and sandy matter.

The low-lying mascon areas of Mars are light-coloured and its dark areas, with some possible minor exceptions, are un-related to surface relief: they may be high or low, cratered or uncratered, and bear no resemblance to the lunar *maria*.

The 'geography' of Mars

Ge is the Greek for the Earth, *Ares* for Mars, and so the proper term for Martian 'geography' is *areography*; but since several planets have been or are being mapped the word 'geography' is coming to be used in a generalised sense as a description of any solid planetary surface. And so it will be here.

Our knowledge of the geography of Mars rests almost wholly on the TV survey by *Mariner 9*. Launched from Cape Kennedy on 30 May 1971, it had to take over the programme of its scheduled companion *Mariner 8*, which failed at the start. *Mariner 9* entered an orbit about Mars on 13 November 1971 and remained operational until 27 October 1972. During this time it transmitted over 7,300 pictures, of which 1,500 were taken with a wide-angle camera with a resolution of 1–3km (depending on the variable distance from the planet). The resolution of the narrow-angle camera was ten times greater.[167]

In November and December the surface of Mars was obscured by a worldwide dust storm, but from January 1972 the visibility improved rapidly, making it possible to cover the entire $142\frac{1}{2}$ million square kilometres of the planet's surface over about a half of the Martian year. At the present epoch—it has not always been so—Mars has no seas, and so its land area is only a little smaller than that of the Earth (roughly 149 million square km).

The processed pictures have been used for the compilation of maps, ranging from 1 : 250,000 to 1 : 250,000,000 in scale, but more detailed information has now become available from the *Viking* mission. Martian latitudes are measured the same way as on Earth, from the equator to the poles: north ($+$) and south ($-$), but a different convention has been adopted for longitudes. The Martian prime meridian is fixed by the centre of Airy-O, a $\frac{1}{2}$-km craterlet within the well-defined larger ring named Airy after the Astronomer Royal particularly associated with the Greenwich Meridian. From this great circle the longitudes are reckoned westwards through 360°. Martian longitudes are always west.[168]

In the absence of sea-level an artificial zero level has been chosen: the partial CO_2 pressure of 6.1mb (4.58mmHg) which marks the triple point of water. Water does not normally occur in liquid phase at lower pressures. But since the atmosphere of Mars seems to contain appreciable proportions of other gases (p 132), this convention has lost some of its initial pertinence. Altitudes above and below this reference level are further estimated on the assumption that the scale height, over which the barometric pressure is reduced by a factor of $1/e$ (e = base of natural logarithms ~ 2.72) is 10km. Neither the barometric pressures nor the scale height are fixed quantities, so that this method of measuring altitudes is at best approximate. Elevations and barometric pressures can be deduced from the occultation data, and the latter directly by measuring the depth of the CO_2 absorption bands.

The timing of radar echoes is another way of tackling the

issue, and relative heights can be calculated, as on the Moon, from the length of shadows. None of these devices are fool-proof but their results can be checked against each other, and contour accuracy of 500 metres can be obtained from wide angle pictures and of 100 metres from narrow-angle ones—or so it is claimed. In the case of canyons and other depressions the assumption is made that the mean angle of the bounding slopes is 10°, which is certainly an underestimate in many cases, so that the result gives no more than the lower limit.

To take two control points as examples, a height of +27.05km has been measured on the summit of *Olympus Mons*, and a low of −2.78km in the area known as *Lunae Palus* on older maps. This gives us some idea of the surface relief of Mars. Other heights are burdened with greater uncertainties but we have a good general picture of Martian topography, and this comprises several 'units' or domains.

The southern hemisphere

The southern hemisphere contains two deep basins: the 2,000-km-wide *Hellas* and the 800-km *Argyre*. These mark some of the lowest points on the Martian surface and resemble the large lunar *maria*, except for being mantled with light-coloured sediments. The rings of Huygens and Schiaparelli are smaller but similar structures, measuring 450km from bounding rampart to bounding rampart. *Isidis Planitia*, just north of the equator and east of the great dark wedge of *Syrtis Major*, is another, incomplete subcircular plain. Its inner ring is 1,100km from crest to crest; it is open to the north-east, where the enclosure merges with the extensive northern plains.

The whole of the northern hemisphere is depressed by about 4km in relation to the southern. As M H Carr puts it:

Mars can be divided into two hemispheres by a plane dipping 50° to the equator such that on one hemisphere are nearly all the volcanic features and sparsely cratered plains and on the other nearly all the densely cratered terrain. The division is not exact, as some cratered terrain occurs in the volcanic hemisphere and vice-versa; nevertheless the difference between the two hemispheres is striking.[169]

South of that line the ground is largely lunar in appearance and was sighted first by *Mariner 4*, giving a misleading impression of Mars. Martian craters, however, are generally flatter and more subdued, bearing witness to erosive action; they usually lack the hummocky surrounds of their lunar counterparts and there is a relative lack of the smaller, clear-cut rings and pits. Crater-chains and crater-valleys, formed by the coalescence of medium-sized rings, are well represented.

Crater distribution is often very uneven and the Martian highlands include such very un-lunar structures such as *Valles Marineris*, a great canyon system which begins in *Noctis Labyrinthus* with a crisscross of U-shaped valleys and extends eastward for about 5,000km. It is partly double and treble, reaching a width of 120km and a depth of at least 5km. It has branched tributaries individually comparable to the Colorado Grand Canyon, and is bounded, chiefly on the north side, by alcoves or *cwms* of monumental proportions. These often send forth into the great trough complete mountain systems—with well-developed primary, secondary and tertiary valleys, bearing witness to energetic water action.

Even more surprising are large isolated hollows with similar characteristics but completely enclosed on all sides. In the east the canyon-lands merge with the so-called *chaotic terrains*. Here subcircular areas 200–300km wide have collapsed into a jumble of troughs, ridges or island heights, usually opening out northwards into wide part-braided channels which follow the slope of the land to the great plains.

There are also huge river systems trending in the same general direction. Unlike the lunar sinuous channels, these dry watercourses of Mars have tributaries, widen and deepen 'downstream' and debouch into the northern plains or other depressed areas. In the region east of *Tharsis* the old river beds lead into two enclosed but intercommunicating depressions some 500km in diameter, which must at one time have been filled with water and formed lakes comparable in size to Lake Victoria. Sandy and bouldery beaches can be seen along their shores. Moreover, these basins are linked by wide channels to the northern plains, and there is nothing in the nature of things to have prevented their waters from overflowing the latter and forming a circumpolar ocean.

Fretted terrain is related to the chaotic terrain, but it has developed along the northern boundary of the plateau lands by the undermining and retreat of the scarp, which averages about 1km high, leaving behind isolated islands, mesas and buttes. In fact the two types of structure may merge with each other, as is the case in *Nilosyrtis Mensae*.

The northern plains

These are characterised by a remarkably level floor covered or mantled with alluvial, aeolian and volcanic deposits. This 'unit' is substantially absent from the south, although *Hellas* (which lies nearly 4km below the zero reference level near the centre) represents terrain similar in outward appearance, if not in origin, and it has a higher southward extension. The plains are sparsely cratered. They are generally light-coloured, but include some dark areas especially nearer the north polar circle.

Conical volcanic piles and domes with summit craters occur in various parts of the surface, including the cratered uplands and the polar regions, but they are especially typical of the great plains, more particularly *Amazonis*, *Arcadia* and *Elysium*. The last-named is, in fact, a vast volcanic complex, ringed by fractures some 300km from the centre of the shield, which is 200–250km wide with a comparatively small cratered cone in the middle. It encompasses some minor domes and volcanic vents. *Arcadia* is a structure of similar dimensions, with ring and radial fractures concentric with shallow central depressions. It looks like a vast shield volcano in the process of collapse, the dome having subsided. *Alba* is another low volcanic dome, wreathed by grooved terrain.

But the chief volcano of Mars is *Olympus Mons*, about 1,000km to the south-east of *Alba*. It measures 600km at the base, and so is no wider than *Alba* (in fact, this figure of 600km seems typical of such structures). *Olympus Mons*, however, is still in the full vigour of youth. Its gently terraced slopes rise 23km above the plain and are bounded by a scarp 1–2km high. It has a complex summit caldera 65km in diameter and may still be active. It bears a marked resemblance to the Hawaiian and Galapagos shield volcanoes except that the latter are much smaller and rise from the ocean floor, the largest Hawaiian pile being only 225km wide at the base and 9km high. The main reason seems to be that the floor of the Pacific is moving and causing its volcanoes to migrate, whereas that of *Amazonis* is stable.[170]

Olympus Mons does not stand alone. It has three somewhat smaller, but otherwise comparable, neighbours: *Arsia Mons*, *Pavonis Mons* and *Ascraeus Mons* (or, to give them their homelier names, the South, Middle and North Spot), ranged along the *Tharsis* Ridge between *Olympus Mons* and *Noctis Labyrinthus*, whose system of fractures extends far southwards and seems to be associated with the *Tharsis* volcanic activity. There are other relatively minor but still impressive volcanoes in this region.

The circumpolar lands are the home of the *etched, pitted* and *laminated terrain*, which consist of sediments overlying an older cratered topography, being eroded chiefly by winds but at some past stage possibly by flowing ice. These layered deposits account for about 2.6 million square kilometres of the Martian surface, with some differences between the northern and southern domains which may be related to the prevalent climatic conditions. Volcanic action may have intervened locally.

The depth of the deposits increases towards the poles and beneath the cap it may reach several kilometres. I have called these deposits 'layered' although in the outer polar halo, which extends down to about latitude 65°, such layering is seldom clearly apparent—at any rate at the limiting resolution of the

Mariner 9 photography. But the sediments could not have been formed all at once, and must have accumulated in layers.

Both the pitted and the etched terrain are the progressive development of what I have described elsewhere[170] as 'cauliflower erosion', the wind getting hold of some weakness in the top layer and nibbling at it until a pit is produced. This must happen on any and every scale, but the pits actually recorded vary in size from about a half to several kiolmetres. They have steep walls with a scarp at the top, and smooth or rough floors. Pitted terrain is not well developed in the north, but in the south it reaches to about latitude 70°.

In the etched terrain some of the buried crater topography is uncovered, sometimes with curious results—such as the so-called 'Inca City', where a high grid of hard dykes stands proud of the eroded landscape. Streamlined ridges known as *yardangs*, flutings and longitudinal *sief* dunes bear clear witness to wind action.[171]

Beneath the poles the quasi-homogeneous 'blanket' is overlain by clearly laminated deposits, exposed by erosion in smooth, confluent terraces 10–50 metres high. As many as 50 of these have been counted in places. The compound thickness of the layers is reckoned at several kilometres. The part of the cap which survives the warm months is depressed, by the weight of either present or past ice sheets, so that the terraces are uptilted at the edges and bear a fancied resemblance to 'stacked plates'. It is not clear whether the layers are rock or ice (water and/or CO_2), interlarded with layers of compacted loess, volcanic ash or some similar fragmentary material.

Indeed, some striated blankets ending up as rough scarps away from the poles do look very much like buried glaciers. There is a strong suspicion that the vast uniform sheet stretching from the south polar icecap to latitude 80° and beyond, between the 240th and 300th meridians, is of this nature. In any case, wind erosion does not satisfactorily explain its high and jagged terminal scarp, for the winds spiral down from the poles. If it consisted of transportable material it ought to thin out gradually, instead of abutting against etched terrain without any transition. In other words, the bright Martian snowcaps may be no more than the tips of icebergs.

Rivers, water and ice erosion

Rivers, lakes and glaciers go together, at least in historical retrospect, and Mars has some spectacular water-carved features.

The interlocking mesh of gullies on the slopes of *Alba* and other mountains is clearly the work of streams; it is unnecessary to strain for other explanations, for the radial grooving of crater and canyon walls mimics in every way the sculpturing by running water familiar on Earth. But the matter is so intriguing that it is well worth while to take a closer look at some of the large river complexes of Mars.

One of these, *Mangala Vallis*, lies in the upland region of *Memnonia* bordering on *Amazonis Planitia*. It may be referred to as the 'Martian Amazon', for, as D J Milton puts it in the JPL *Mariner Mars 1971 Project Final Report* (p 32), 'the volume of flow of the Amazonis channel, which is far from the largest on Mars, must have been at least the proportions of its terrestrial namesake'. It is some 350km long and comprises a system of channels spread over a zone nearly 100km wide. The flow seems to have been northwards, following the slope of the land, so that it would have discharged into the surrounding plains. In the middle part the various channels gather into a broad, flat-bottomed trough and then break up again into a braided configuration, which Milton regards as the most convincing example of water action on Mars.

This braided section of the Martian Amazon is a good replica on a much enlarged scale of the multi-channel course of the Sagavanirtok river in Alaska—the same teardrop islands and intersecting beds, only with everything some ten times larger in the Martian example. The Sagavanirtok is a glacial river, subject to flooding; and enormous temporary rivers, released by the bursting of ice-dammed lakes, did scour parts of Europe and the USA at the end of the Pleistocene Ice Age.

The Channelled Scablands of Washington provide a parallel to the Martian Amazon—in this case even the scale is right. Thus the Martian Amazon must have been a temporary inter-glacial river, but a careful examination of the *Mariner* high-resolution frames will reveal thin meanders on the floors of the broad straths. This not only recalls Schroeter's Valley on the Moon: it is not unusual in the recently-glaciated parts of the Earth, such as the Scottish Highlands.

Such a thin meander stands out even clearer in the *Ma'adim Vallis*, centred at latitude 20°S and longitude 182°. The channel extends over 700km, is very deep and up to 10km broad in its middle course. It has been compared in its depth-to-width ratio to some lunar sinuous rilles, but unlike these it has branched tributaries and broadens downstream. The simple explanation in terms of excavation by running water seems to fall short of the requirements: some other factors must have intervened. It may be that the river followed pre-existent tectonic fractures along which erosion was very rapid, but it is possible that it flowed partly underground until its vaulting roof was undermined and collapsed, as happened in England's Cheddar Gorge.

The chaotic terrains described above have involved collapse over much wider areas and have been explained by the melting of underground ice. But even this hypothesis implies that the Martian upper crust has a Swiss-cheese structure, and if this is correct there need not have been any melting at all. Running water may be burrowing under the overlying strata all the time.

This may also help to solve the problem of the removal of material from the vast canyons, which is estimated at not less than 1.8×10^6 cubic kilometres. It might simply have collapsed into the caves or been washed away by subsurface streams. But if those vast masses of underground ice really exist we must reckon with ice dykes and *pingos* (p 77), which after evapora-tion could form troughs and craters respectively.

Nevertheless, it seems likely that the great *Valles Marineris* are rift-valleys, produced by the parting of the crust when the uplands were raised to compensate for the sinking in the northern plains and, more locally, in *Argyre* and *Hellas*. Movement of tectonic plates provides an alternative explanation. Yet there has obviously been some caving-in, as is testified by the rows of rimless pits continuing and/or paralleling the trends of the troughs.

The retreat of the canyon walls and of the terminal scarp of the uplands in the northern fretted terrain is, however, ascribed to artesian sapping: undermining by water and/or ice at the contact with an impervious stratum. In one picture of *Valles Marineris* the spectrometer scan missed a high, probably volcanic peak. Its summit must stand a couple of kilometres above the canyon scarp, and it looks very much as if a substantial glacier were descending its east side. Artesian sapping may also have broadened the river valleys.

Julian Kane (Hofstra University, New York) and collaborators have spotted a system of alpine mountains centred at latitude 76.6° and longitude 72.7°, bearing the marks of recent glaciation with cirques or *cwms* and 'horns' at the meeting of the ridges.[172]

The signs of water action on the surface are unmistakeable, as in the case of the 400-km branched sinuous channel *Nirgal Vallis*, north of *Argyre*. This is very like the *arroyos* or dry desert water-courses of the south-western USA, except again for scale. The channel is 5–6km wide in its lower course, where it drains into a crater. Smaller tributaries below the limit of resolution are suspected. Moreover, it does not seem that the darkness of the channel can be accounted for by shadow alone. It contains some dark material, probably of the same kind as in the irregular blotches nearby. In fact, this looks very much like vegetation crowding into a river valley in a dry climate (*see Plates 10, 11*).

The 'canals': illusion or substance?

This may be an appropriate place to consider briefly the problem of the 'canals'. It is clear enough that the spidery geometrical grids depicted by Lowell and collaborators[173] were based on optical illusion. But this is not quite the end of the story.

R S Richardson[174] and Edison Pettit did not believe in the 'canals'. Yet, to his astonishment, the latter did see them quite clearly in 1939 with the 60-inch Mt Wilson reflector, as olive-green lines. Richardson was using the same instrument, and described his experience of 3 June 1956 as follows:

> This morning the disk had a peculiar aspect which I had not noticed before. There were innumerable irregular blue lines extending across the bright red regions like veins through some mineral. Several minutes passed before it occurred to me that these markings must be canals. I was taken completely by surprise . . .

It is true that *Mariner 9* and, most recently, the *Vikings*, have shown nothing of the kind, but that is not decisive. The *Mariner* pictures in particular were monochrome, and orange monochrome at that. As we have seen with the examples of the TLPs and the lights on Mercury's dark side, observations have a way of surviving their critics and detractors. It must, however, be emphasised that the lines seen by Richardson were 'irregular'.

Atmosphere and climate

The remarkable success of the *Viking* landers has superseded much of the earlier atmospheric research, but their measurements are highly localised in time and space, and we still have to call on the old observations in assessing the global situation. The conclusions drawn from the *Mariner 9* mission rest on three sets of data:

(*a*) Radio occultations; (*b*) Telescopic and spacecraft spectroscopy; (*c*) The temperature profile obtained from UV airglow measurements.[175(a)]

All this involves certain theoretical assumptions and has consequent limitations which continue to apply to the interpretation of the observations made by the *Viking* orbiters.

By such methods it has been found that the 'air' of Mars contains mainly carbon dioxide (CO_2), a little oxygen and traces of water vapour in the lower reaches, and higher up a variable proportion of ozone (O_3). The ozone is up to 1 per cent of our atmospheric content and seems to be inversely related to the abundance of water vapour. Finally there is some carbon monoxide (CO), produced by the dissociation of CO_2 by the UV; and a thin outer halo of hydrogen, which may in part be similarly derived from water and in part from the Solar Wind. The instrumented module of the Soviet probe *Mars 6* entered the atmosphere in 1974 and reported a large proportion of a 'neutral gas' (thought to be argon), whose percentage was doubtfully estimated at between 10 and 35.[175(b)] No nitrogen was detected in any of these investigations.

On-the-spot atmospheric sampling by the *Viking 1* lander has yielded the following composition: 2–3 per cent nitrogen; $1\frac{1}{2}$–2 per cent argon; 0.3 per cent oxygen; a small, diurnally variable amount of water vapour; some carbon monoxide; and about one part per hundred-million of nitrogen monoxide (NO). The remainder is CO_2. Lower (N_2O) and higher (NO_2) oxides of nitrogen, as well as nitrous and nitric acids, are suspected in concentrations too low for detection by the Viking instruments.[176] These compounds are biologically important, as in being precipitated on the surface they would produce nitrates and nitrites, and so nitrogen in forms accessible to assimilation by living organisms.[177]

A barometric pressure of about 7.7 millibars has been found at both landing sites. This is 2.6mb above the triple point of water, and so allows water to assume liquid form if only transitorily owing to intense evaporation. But there is no similar limitation on capillary condensation in, say, plant tissues. The *Mariner 9 Final Report* puts the ground barometric pressure at between 3mb for *Olympus Mons* and 11mb for the depression of Hellas (an altitude range of some 28km), but the figures obtained from the S-band occultations at grazing angles are somewhat higher, namely 4–14mb.[178]

The *Vikings* have confirmed water-ice absorptions at the

polar caps, first identified by Kuiper in 1947, and the relatively high abundance of water suggested by some previous observations. It must be appreciated that only airborne vapour is directly accessible to the spectroscope, and its content is necessarily very low in the cold and thin Martian atmosphere. This content is set an upper limit by the saturation point, or the partial vapour pressure at a given temperature: any excess will condense more or less at once.

The air temperatures recorded by *Viking 1* during its first day on Mars ranged from $-86°C$ just after dawn to $-30°C$, the maximum occurring some 3–4 hours after the local noon. Saturated water vapour pressures in the upper range of these temperatures are:

$-69°C$	0.0031 millibars
-40	0.128
-30	0.380
-20	1.046
-10	2.587

This shows that the pressure rises rapidly with temperature, but at $-69°C$ it accounts for barely 0.04 per cent of the atmospheric composition. At still lower temperatures the maximum possible water content becomes infinitesimally small. As a result the lower atmosphere is readily oversaturated, as is amply proven by extensive clouds, of which more presently.

Rime and snow are certain, dew and perhaps rain at least possible. The temperature gradient (adiabatic lapse) on Mars is about 4.6°C per kilometre. Thus, if we start with $-86°C$ near the surface, 10km higher up the air temperature should drop (there may be inversions) to $-132°C$. During the descent of *Viking 1* a low of $-138°C$ was actually registered at an altitude of 135km.[179] The 'cold trap' for water vapour is very effective on Mars, practically none of it reaching the upper atmosphere.

Indeed, the Martian air is so cold that even its principal constituent, CO_2, is in the condition of precipitable vapour, which is also subject to the 'cold trap' effect. At a certain height the bulk of the CO_2 is frozen out into a haze of fine crystals, which evaporate as they drop and are replaced by new ones brought by rising air currents. This is what I have described as a 'fuming atmosphere' (1973).[180]

Such a haze was observed by *Mariner 9*, and is clearly visible in the oblique view of *Argyre* taken by the *Viking 1* orbiter. The altitude of the high haze, which may correspond to the so-called 'violet layer', is 25–40km—but the same photograph also shows an intense horizon haze of uncertain composition. It is clearly this low haze that is responsible for the unexpected brightness of the Martian sky in the lander panoramas.[181]

When the first of these was assembled by computer from the composite filter views in red, green and blue, the sky looked pale-blue and the ground had a rusty-red hue reminiscent of the soil of Somerset and Devon in England, or of African laterite. In the opinion of James Pollack of the Ames Research Center, however, Mars could not have a blue sky because of the insufficient molecular (Rayleigh) scattering by its thin atmosphere, and the sky brightness had to be attributed to a suspension of fine reddish dust.[182] Later versions of the surface panoramas were corrected accordingly to a salmon-pink sky and a ground of an intense vermilion, which does not look quite creditable. In fact, one of the views includes the American flag on the lander, and the blue background to the stars in this flag is purple, which indicates a colour shift towards the red.[183]

Martian dust-storms are yellow, not red, and it is well known that when Mars is photographed through colour filters its surface is usually more or less invisible in blue and quite invisible in the UV exposures, which show atmospheric features only. This is an indisputable indication that the Martian atmosphere strongly scatters the shorter wavelengths of the Solar spectrum. This need not be due to molecular scattering: fine smoke from dry wood looks blue without being molecular. The effect probably resides in the high haze mentioned above and identified with the 'violet layer', local condensations in which are known as 'blue clouds'. But it would suggest that the sky of Mars is in fact blue, or rather violet-blue, and also that not much of the Solar UV can reach the surface. Of course, our sky may also look salmon-pink at the horizon; but it seems that the original version of the Martian ground panoramas was nearer the truth.

The atmosphere of Mars differs in many important respects from that of the Earth, and not in composition alone. With the surface gravity reduced by about $\frac{2}{5}$ the pressure gradient should, other things being equal, be $2\frac{1}{2}$ times less steep, so the Martian atmosphere would be expected to extend this much higher than ours. Yet its main constituent, CO_2, is a vapour, some of which seems to be seasonally precipitated in the polar caps. As these wax and wane the total mass of the Martian atmosphere, and so the barometric pressures and atmospheric composition, should fluctuate in the same cycle. Moreover, owing to the high orbital eccentricity (p 119), the global temperatures on Mars are lowest near aphelion, which falls close to the northern summer and southern winter—and so to the time when the *Vikings* landed. If so, the figure of 7.7mb measured by them would not be far above the possible minimum.

The tiered structure of the Martian atmosphere, outlined by the hazes, means that the atmosphere is, as it were, cut short by the CO_2 cold trap, above which its total pressure cannot exceed the partial pressure of CO_2 at the fuming level. Yet the CO_2 condensed in the fuming haze is not removed from the atmosphere and weighs just as much as it would uncondensed, so that the barometric pressures below this level remain the same as if the haze and the consequent pressure jump did not exist.

A further point that seems to have been systematically overlooked is that in a substantially CO_2 atmosphere CO_2 cannot condense into clouds by convection, by orographic uplift (climbing a mountain), or by contact between cold and warm air masses, to which the formation of water clouds in our air is commonly due. The reason is very simple: warm CO_2 and cold CO_2 are both CO_2, and the problem of over-saturation does not arise.[184]

If a warm air mass which is 95 per cent CO_2 comes into contact with a cold air mass in which no CO_2 condensation has occurred, the chilling of the former cannot result in the formation of clouds. On the contrary, a pre-existent CO_2 haze in the cold mass may be caused to dissipate by the heat transfer from the warmer mass. It need, therefore, cause no surprise that all convective clouds observed on Mars have been found to be composed of water ice—the temperatures were too high for CO_2 condensation. On the other hand, CO_2 veils may form when the temperatures are sufficiently low, eg over the polar caps, though these veils too seem to be predominantly aqueous.[185]

Flocculated clouds, often thrown into waves by topographic relief, sometimes in two or three superimposed layers moving in different directions, occur mainly in winter in the middle latitudes of 30–40°. Nearer the pole the surface is engulfed in general haze but can still be made out up to some 60° of latitude, beyond which the 'polar hood' forms a wholly opaque blanket, hiding the cap. The hood begins to develop in the autumn and to disperse with the coming of the spring, revealing the shining snow-cap underneath. As stated, water ice has been identified spectroscopically in the caps and it has been established by the *Viking 1* orbiter that the summer temperatures of the north cap are too high for CO_2 condensation.

Massive clouds, have, however, been observed in the summer as well, and at much lower latitudes. During the approach of *Viking 1* a huge area about *Tharsis* and *Olympus Mons*, just north of the equator, was completely smothered by rippling cloudbanks, only the heads of the great volcanoes rising above them. Mists, fogs and clouds regularly form in the evening or mornings in some localities, including the calderas and lower slopes of the giant volcanoes.

The highest temperature recorded by *Mariner 9* was 285°K ($+12$°C) during a northern autumn, but temperatures of up to 32°C have been measured from Earth in the Martian tropics near perihelion. Such radiometric temperatures (obtained from the IR measurements), if not wholly unambiguous, refer to the ground. But the temperatures recorded by the *Viking* landers are air temperatures, taken about 2 metres above the surface in moderate wind. On Mars this makes a very considerable difference as the air is thin, has a low heat capacity and stays very cold.

As a check-up on this I have calculated the theoretical surface temperatures at aphelion, assuming a 10 per cent obscuration and an albedo of 0.15. For the Sun directly overhead the temperature is $+13.5°C$; at $45°$ elevation $-10°C$; at $30°$ $-32°C$. These temperatures are much higher than the *Viking* figures and are very sensitive to albedo and slope. A boulder facing the Sun at right-angles may be quite warm on the sunward side, regardless of latitude even at aphelion, while its shadow side will be many degrees below freezing point. Thus Mars, like the Moon, is a world of microclimates; it will have oases of warmth in the lee of mountains facing the Sun, crater bowls and deep valleys, sheltered from the prevailing winds.

Carl Sagan and other investigators forecast strong winds on Mars with speeds of up to 250km per hour,[187] but the *Viking* landers have recorded only mild winds from about 3–27km per hour, with an occasional gust or two of 40–60km per hour. High winds approximating to the expected velocities have, however, been inferred from the rapid cloud movements in the upper atmospheric levels near the summit of *Olympus Mons*.

Vulcanism and dust storms

In the search for thermally abnormal areas *Mariner 9* discovered 27 localities, warmer or colder than their surroundings by up to $13°C$.[188] In most cases the difference could be accounted for by slope, elevation, ground structure or albedo; but the higher temperatures found at the south-western edge of the *Argyre* basin ($+10°$) and in a flow-channel in *Acidalia* ($+13°$) could not be so explained. No volcanic 'hot spots' have been identified, but it should be remembered that a lake of lava at $1,500°K$

would have to be at least 200 metres in diameter and lie within
the radiometer field of view to yield an observed rise of 3°C, so
that 'even if Mars had twice the volcanic activity of the Earth
the probability of observing such a feature would be very
small'.[189]

On the other hand, telescopic observations indicate powerful
volcanic eruptions.[190]

Grey circular clouds with a point origin, spreading out
mushroom-wise to diameters of 100–200km, were seen by
Antoniadi in 1910 and 1911, and by Saheki, Murayama and
other Japanese observers in 1950 and 1952. The 1950 cloud
reached a diameter of 750km and covered much of *Erydania*
and *Electris* (old nomenclature). These clouds were also
observed to fluctuate in colour between grey, white and yellow
in a matter of days, which supports the volcanic interpretation.

More surprising are the brilliant flares reported in 1937, 1951,
1954 and 1958 from Japan and the USA. They seem to be
particularly associated with the area between *Tithonium Chasma*
and *Melas Chasma* in the central part of *Valles Marineris*, and
with *Schiaparelli*. This localisation rules out explanation by
meteoritic impact. Saheki estimated the 1951 flare to have had
the brightness of a sixth-magnitude star and endured for 5
minutes. Nothing comparable is known on Earth short of a
hydrogen-bomb explosion; but fissile radioactive materials
could become concentrated by geological processes into a
natural atomic pile, which could occasionally blow up. In fact,
such a prehistoric reactor has been discovered by French
scientists in Gabon, Africa.

There may seem to be little reason to associate dust storms
with vulcanism. Winds can and do raise local clouds of dust on
Mars, and there is ample evidence of vast deposits of fine,
rock-flour material resembling our loess, as well as of strong
and persistent winds, resulting in dunes and other structures
well-known from our deserts. Yet planet-wide dust storms such
as greeted *Mariner 9* in 1971 are not so easy to explain. Not
only would they require typhoons or tornadoes of unimaginable

ferocity, but their mode of origin, scale and relative rarity put a great strain on the wind hypothesis.

The following description by C F Capen[191] bears this out:

> The yellow clouds of 1909, 1911, 1924, 1939, 1956 and 1971 favoured the Hellas–Noachis region. The initial formation appears relatively bright and wide and later takes on a yellowish-white hue. The physical aspects of the phenomenon are composed of at least three visible parts: the bright white-yellow core of the storm, the large encompassing ochre obscuration of surface features, and the small peripheral blue-white clouds, which appear to be associated with a mature yellow storm.

It is not all dust. Condensation is obviously involved, which must indeed be expected, as dust particles provide condensation nuclei for atmospheric moisture. A super-tornado might generate such effects, but the description is highly suggestive of a great volcanic outburst, which could readily project vast amounts of ash into the high atmosphere, as did the Krakatoa blow-up in 1883.

The truth of the matter is that we do not really understand the mechanism of these great storms. Even the relationship between them and the Martian loess is unclear.

The settling of a yellow dust cloud ought to make the underlying ground brighter, but the reverse holds true: it usually darkens. This effect was observed telescopically by E C Slipher[192] and has been confirmed by *Mariner 9*. Moreover, the latter has shown that it is usually the ravines and depressions, which may be expected to provide catchments for blown dust, that darken.

This brings us to the further problem of the variable features of Mars and the possibility of life there.

Variable features

The 200 years or so of systematic telescopic study bear ample witness to both seasonal and secular variability of the dark features of Mars. Complicated colour changes have likewise

been reported, notably by Antoniadi, observing at Meudon
during the close approaches (oppositions) of Mars in 1922 and
1924.[193] Colours and colour variations are always a fruitful
ground for dispute, but Antoniadi's evidence cannot be dismissed out of hand; and my own modest filter observations
show the presence of a green element in at least some tropical
'*maria*' and of a red one nearer the poles—which proves
nothing at all with regard to their nature, except that it differs
in the two cases. For instance, some boulders in the *Viking 1*
close-ups of the surface are distinctly greenish.

The telescopic consensus is that as the polar hood disperses
and the snow-cap begins to recede in spring, the dark features
become more prominent with the advancing season. Percival
Lowell, the enthusiast of the 'canals', thought that water was
being pumped along these from the melting cap to irrigate the
Martian 'world athirst' in a 'wave of quickening', advancing
at a rate of some 40km per day from the pole to the equator,
which it overruns by 1,500km or more. By then it is late autumn,
and the process begins in reverse at the other pole. Those who
dismissed the 'canals' still explained this as the seasonal revival
of vegetation, due to the atmospheric moisture released from
the cap.

The reality of the 'wave of quickening' has been questioned.
We will recall from p 136 that the surface polewards of latitude
30° is clouded during the winter, and the dispersal of these
clouds will alone suffice to darken the '*maria*'. The dispersal,
however, is due to the lengthening hours of daylight and rising
atmospheric temperatures and proceeds from the equator to
the pole, as also does the seasonal renewal of vegetation on
Earth—which is the reverse of the Martian situation.

The pictures of the low southern latitudes taken by *Mariners
6* and *7* show cratered panoramas of a remarkably uniform
albedo. But the same areas televised by *Mariner 9* in the
autumn are blotched, streaked and speckled with dark markings. In any case the probe followed the northern hemisphere
from the early spring to the late autumn, and confirmed beyond
a shadow of doubt that the dark markings do expand in the

warmer season.[194] Striking changes have been recorded within a period of a week or so.

The question is, what is the true nature of these markings and the cause of change?

The first point is that, with the exception of the polar collar, whose reality stands confirmed, and a few minor features (eg about *Kasei Vallis*), the dusky areas seen in the distant views of Mars dissolve in the close-ups into swarms of dark 'streaks' and 'splotches' which, like birds of a feather, flock together. The streaks are elongated markings 10 or more km long, frequently in the form of 'crater-tails', which may be comet- or fan-shaped or resemble the flame of a candle, including its central and peripheral shading. But straight, rectilinear and shredded or wavy streaks also occur, and need not be associated with vertical relief. Splotches are irregular or rounded, often found within craters, centrally or on the side, and may 'wash over' the walls into the 'intersticial ground'. Some dark areas have jagged boundaries with sharp, triangular saw-teeth.

There are also bright streaks and crater-tails, which are usually straighter, narrower and longer than the dark ones. The two systems are not always in agreement and may intersect at various angles. There are no bright splotches.

Mariner 9 recorded no changes in the bright streaks, but only a development of the dark features which, having reached their maximum extent, remained unchanged.

As Carl Sagan and collaborators state,[195] the explanation by growth and decay of vegetation is 'impossible to disprove from the Earth or from Martian orbit, because the hypothetical Martian organisms can have a wide range of conceivable attributes'. Nevertheless, his study group prefers the alternative explanation 'in terms of the alternate deposition and deflation of windblown dust having detectable contrast with respect to basement material.'[196]

Indeed, some of these features are closely paralleled by the wind patterns in terrestrial deserts, only the contrasts and the scale are much greater on Mars. Windblown material is unquestionably involved, and some of it is certainly loess.

But winds can also carry moisture, salts and various gases. Bright, yellow storms are well known; there is no record of dark dust clouds. The alternative explanation—bright dust being blown off a dark 'basement material'—may do in some cases. Thus the windward crater walls could be blown clear of the dust coating. Somehow, however, it is always the *inside*, not the outside, walls that are denuded. Then again, such a 'splotch' due to the uncovering of the dark rocks could not possibly 'wash over' the crater walls to the lee side to form a tail, where the bright dust would naturally accumulate—as it does in the bright streaks. The crater would therefore have to be the source of the dark dust—yet the markings outside the crater are often quite unrelated to it.

Let us now turn to the polar collar. It is made up of a nearly-continuous 'splotchy' mass. The basement material is a light-coloured deposit. So where would the dark dust come from?

The dust storms show clearly that the bright dust is the mobile element. Why, then, has not a single instance been found of its encroaching on a dark marking? The answer seems to be that the observations were made between the northern spring and the autumn; and it may be noted that only bright streaks were found in the southern polar regions and only dark ones in the northern. We would thus have a situation where only the dark dust is blown by the winds during the warm seasons, and only the bright dust with the advent of winter.

With all due respect to Professor Sagan, this does not make much sense. If, on the other hand, the dark markings are primarily vegetation springing up along the path of a moist wind, which could be quite gentle, everything falls neatly into place. The bright streaks will still be the product of Sagan's cold, dry winter winds—cold air necessarily has a low saturation point. The prevailing wind direction may be expected to vary with the seasons, which could explain the intersecting patterns of bright and dark streaks. Clouds have been photographed in the calderas and canyons, which must contain sources of water vapour. Similarly, volcanic springs may be expected in some craters. Evaporation on Mars is intense, and the rising vapour will be picked up by the wind and carried over the wall, producing a dark tail. The 'shredded streaks' on the outside slopes of the great plateau of *Syrtis Major* bear a strong resemblance to the pattern of forests on the slopes of the Andes photographed from Earth-satellite vehicles.

If this reading of the situation is correct, it means that there is life on Mars NOW—for which indeed there is other evidence.

This life seems to be at rather a low ebb, and would have been much more luxuriant and varied in the halcyon days when those big floods were spilling down the river channels (p 128). Still, many terrestrial plants—including such unlikely ones as millet and cucumber—thrive in the Martian conditions created in laboratory experiments, and Martian plants would be better adapted to Mars.[197]

The existence of a fauna is much more problematic. Rotifers and tardigrades are tiny creatures that would be capable of withstanding the climatic rigours of Martian environment. Larger animals could spend the cold dark hours in deep burrows. The real hitch is the low atmospheric oxygen content. It has, however, been suggested that, like some of our bog plants, those of Mars may retain in their bodies the oxygen produced in the photosynthesis of carbohydrates, in which case the hypothetical Martian animals could obtain the oxygen they need from the plants. Alternatively, oxidation may be wholly or partly replaced by *anaerobic glycolysis* as a source of energy, as in deep-diving turtles.

Sagan has summarised his own version of Martian biology in a paper, *The long winter of Martian biology*.[198] He contends that the polar caps, and at the present epoch the massive north cap in particular, contain vast amounts of volatiles, chiefly CO_2. If the residual north cap is taken to be 1km thick, with a mean density of $1g/cm^3$, its complete vaporisation would yield 1kg of gas for every square centimetre of the Martian surface, and 'there would be as much atmosphere on Mars as on the Earth'. He reckons that this will happen through the precession of the equinoxes (p 120). The critical period would be between 12,500 and 25,000 years from now, when the sequence of the seasons in the two hemispheres will be reversed. The evaporation of the cap would raise the barometric pressures and overall temperatures so that the process would be self-accelerating, and Mars would enjoy its 'great summer'. V I Moroz in Russia has somewhat similar ideas.[199]

Indeed, while the density of small impact craters on the floors of the wide channels scoured by the *Chryse* floods bears clear witness to their great antiquity, some other, smaller water channels look fresh and unscathed. Harold Masursky, who has made an extensive study of these features, has come out with the opinion that Mars has experienced many 'pluvial periods' when temperatures were sufficiently high and the atmosphere sufficiently dense to allow rivers to flow.[200]

There is no present way of gauging the relative frequency of these periods and their possible relation to the precession of the equinoxes. That the latter must have some effect cannot be denied, but personally I doubt if this would be enough to refill the giant *arroyos* and turn the Martian lowlands into seas. Something more like Earth's orogenetic periods, with intensified volcanic activity and gas exhalation (p 32) seems to come nearer the mark. Such periods may recur every 500 million years or so, when things would liven up for some millions of years and gradually backslide into something like the present situation.

The *Vikings* in search of life

Vikings 1 and *2*, both in operation at the time of writing (September 1976) are of identical design and embody two parts: an *orbiter* and a *lander*. The former is an octagonal box 2.4 × 3.3 metres, with 4 solar battery panels extending like wings to a span of 9.7 metres. It is a dual-purpose craft, weighing 2,325kg. On the one hand, its object is to convey the lander to Mars, launch it for landing and then relay to Earth the data obtained by it on the surface. On the other, it operates independently on the lines of *Mariner 9*, but with increased sophistication, for a period of 120 days.

The lander is hexagonal, with four shock-absorbing legs. It measures 2 × 3 metres, stands about 2 metres high, and weighs 576kg. It has an operational life of 90 days. At atmospheric entry it is protected by a heat-resistant capsule, later discarded, and it lands by a combination of a discardable parachute and retro-rocket action.

The lander is an extremely ingenious piece of engineering, equipped for atmospheric and surface sampling, meteorological, seismic and magnetic observations, as well as three biological experiments: *pyrolitic release*, *labelled release* and *gas exchange* tests. In each of them a small quantity of Martian soil, scooped up by a grab device mounted on an extendable boom, is delivered to a miniature processing laboratory.

Pyrolitic release is designed to examine the fixation of CO_2 and CO labelled with radioactive carbon-14 (C14) by possible micro-organisms in the soil. After an incubation period of some days in artificial sunlight, the sample is heated to 120°C to drive off the excess gases; a further pyrolysis or 'heat cracking' is carried out at 625°C, and after purging with helium the sample is reheated to 700°C. In this way any organic compounds that may be present are broken up and oxidised to CO_2; the absorbed C14 is then ascertained by a radiation counter.

Labelled release is basically similar, but the experiment is carried out with a mixture of radioactively-labelled organic nutrients added to the soil.

In the *gas exchange* test, no assumptions are made regarding the nature of the putative organic processes, and only the changes in the composition of the atmosphere over the sample are studied after a period of incubation. For control, the tests are made on heat-sterilised soil.

Each lander mounts 2 TV cameras of novel design for black-and-white and colour imaging (using a red, green and blue filter). These scan the sorroundings over a full circle, slowly, a narrow strip at a time, by means of a small tilting mirror. Image definition of unsurpassable excellence has been obtained in this way, but at a price: the cameras are unable to register moving objects such as animals or dust-devils. Even a tortoise would produce no more than a smudge.[201]

Viking 1 was launched on 20 August 1975 into a Hohmann orbit that took it halfway round the Sun, entering an elliptical Mars-synchronous orbit with a close point of 900 miles and a far one of 22,000 miles on 19 June 1976. The landing sites originally selected proved too rough. Eventually, however, the lander touched down without a mishap in the vast plain of *Chryse Planitia* on 20 July 1976, on stone-strewn level desert ground with small sand dunes, and obtained some technically beautiful panoramas with a horizon 3km away.[202] The seismic apparatus was out of action, and there was some trouble, subsequently rectified, with the soil-scoop.

The three life-seeking experiments were successfully performed, with a positive reaction in each case suggesting biological activity at the level of dry Antarctic soils.[203] This was corroborated by the negative result of the control test, but no organic compounds were found in the soil analysis. This, however, is not very sensitive and would fail to detect the presence of bacteria in ordinary garden soil.[204]

A further objection raised was that certain chemicals, such as peroxides and superoxides (eg of sodium) could simulate the observed effects without the intervention of life. Appropriate experiments to test this idea are under way, but the existence of these compounds on the surface of Mars is highly improbable, especially as the thin atmosphere contains only 0.3 per cent of free oxygen.

On 2 September 1976 *New Scientist* (p 276) summed up the situation thus: 'Only an exotic catalytic effect, and one presently inexplicable, might deal with these effects without the hypothesis of life on Mars.'

Viking 1 is to repeat the experiments. Meanwhile the first inorganic analysis of the soil has yielded the following result in weight percentages: aluminium, 2 to 7; silicon, 15 to 30; iron, 14 ± 2; calcium, 3 to 8; titanium, 0.5 to 2; sulphur, up to 6; potassium, 0 to 2; chlorine, 0 to 3. An upper limit of 10 per cent has been set for phosphorus, which is an important component of nucleic acids and some enzymes, and so vital to our type of life.[205]

Viking 2, launched on 9 September 1975, entered the same kind of orbit on 7 August 1976 and set down its lander in *Utopia*, 7,400km north-west and 20° of latitude north of the first landing site. The module came to rest at an angle of 8° among what has been described as a 'forest of boulders', many of metre size, which it succeeded in avoiding. Its seismometers are working, but have to date recorded no Mars-quakes. The biological tests have given results generally similar to those of *Viking 1*—life-like reactions, but no bodies! Its general character is not unsimilar to that of *Chryse Planitia*; but there are no mesas to be seen on the horizon and the boulders are much larger and full of holes—like Swiss cheese, which stamps them as gas-rich vesicular lavas. An intriguing feature of the site is a small flow-channel, which must be recent to have survived the drifting loess.

Meanwhile, with the landers successfully emplaced and operational, the *Viking 1* orbiter has been placed in an advancing non-synchronous orbit with a lower periapsis of 500 miles (800km) above the surface, the other orbiter acting as a relay station. The new orbit takes it over the polar regions and allows a systematic photo-survey of the entire globe.[206] The resolution so far achieved is 2–20 times better than in the *Mariner 9* pictures, but the smallest accessible objects remain larger than a football stadium.[207]

Nevertheless, areas previously thought to be smooth and undifferentiated have emerged as full of minor detail: bumps, stream-gullies and small craters. An interesting feature is striated aprons on the sides of the canyons in *Valles Marineris*.[208] These are closely comparable to the aprons of Tsiolkovsky on the Moon, and their nature is in some doubt. Landslides are not usually striated: this is characteristic of weakly coherent flow. A wet landslide might produce such an effect. On the other hand, large deposits of underground ice are expected on Mars, and have indeed been invoked to explain the *Chryse* floods (p 129). Thus these aprons could easily be 'rock glaciers', or the remains of rock glaciers after the ice has evaporated.

The survey is still in progress.

The potato moonlets

The two midget, potato-shaped moons, Phobos and Deimos, do not affect the surface condition of Mars; but they are part of its scene, whose description would be incomplete if they were left out.

Mariner 9 provided good photographs of these curious bodies, especially Phobos. They seem to be captured asteroids, although their close proximity to Mars and the small inclinations of their orbits (1.1° and 1.8° respectively) to the planet's equator present almost insuperable dynamical difficulties to such an origin. According to the best data[209] their measurements are: Phobos—27.0 × 21.4 × 19.2km; mass 17.4 × 10^{15}kg approx; Deimos—15.0 × 12.0 × 11.0km; mass 3.11 × 10^{15}kg approx.

A density of 3 is assumed, as the moonlets seem to consist of hard rock, with hard surfaces pockmarked with small craters, which may be due to impact or degassing. They are very dark, with albedoes of 0.05 (Phobos) and 0.06 (Deimos), and would seem to be fragments of a larger body. They have captured rotations and revolve about Mars at the mean distances from its centre of 9,133km and 23,490km, in 7.65 and 30.30 hours respectively. Since Phobos outruns the axial spin of Mars, it rises in the west and sets in the east after a mean interval of 11 hours 2 minutes and 6 seconds. Deimos rises 'decently' in the east and has a mean synodic period of 62 hours 3 minutes and 50 seconds, so that it will stay in the Martian sky for over 30 hours at a time.

8

The Outer Planets

Beyond Mars there is a gap of about 4AU without a major planet, which is replaced by a belt of asteroids, densest between 2.7 and 3.2AU, with some stragglers on both sides of these limits. The belt includes about a score of minor planets with diameters over 100km, some 40,000 asteroids (many of which are irregular chunks of rock) and pebble-sized stuff, obviously derived from the break-up of a larger mass or masses. There is indeed some evidence that a major planet came to grief here some 500 million years ago (p 17).

Meanwhile the asteroidal belt presents a hazard to space navigation, although less serious than expected. It has already been successfully negotiated by *Pioneers 10* and *11* on the way to Jupiter, first and largest of the Outer Planets, and roughly halfway between the Earth and the Sun in size. Jupiter is followed by three lesser giants—Saturn, Uranus and Neptune —and the small pseudo-terrestrial world of Pluto, which definitely does not fit into this company. The most important data relating to them are found in Table III.

The existence of further planets beyond Pluto is suspected. R A Mackenzie of the Isle of Wight Astronomical Society suggests, on the basis of comet families and unexplained irregularities in the motions of Uranus and Neptune, that there may be as many as five of them, intermediate in size between the terrestrial and Outer Planets, the nearest two being at about 53 and 77AU. Similar conclusions have been reached by others.

The difficulty of discovering such objects is twofold: optical and dynamical. They are very faint, and they move very slowly. The apparent motion of Neptune among the stars is about 2°

per year, and Mackenzie's nearest trans-Plutonian planet with
an orbital period of 390 years would make less than 1°. Neptune
and Pluto were discovered from the perturbing effects on their
inward neighbours, and the slower the movements the more
difficult such effects are to determine.

Even within the known confines of the Solar System observation becomes less and less effective as we move away from the
Sun; our knowledge declines in proportion, and all data are
burdened with growing uncertainties. The *Pioneers* have found
that the mass estimate of Jupiter's system was two Moon-
masses short. This is perhaps not too bad an error for so large
a mass, but as it affects chiefly the Galilean satellites it becomes
considerable. Their masses are now known to within a few
per cent, but their diameters (except that of Io) remain in
doubt.

In Table III (p 167) the intensity of sunlight is quoted in
mean full Moons (as the brightness of the real full Moon
varies).[210] At the Earth's orbit the Sun is as bright as 436,500
full Moons packed together; by the time we reach Jupiter this
figure drops to 16,440. Yet even at the mean distance of Pluto,
where the Sun subtends an angle of 49″, or roughly the same as
Jupiter does in our skies, sunlight is equivalent to 251 full
Moons—much brighter than any artificial lighting, and perfectly adequate for all visual purposes *there*. Telescopically,
however, this loss of light is very serious.

As Table III also shows, in terms of the Solar Constant the
heat of sunrays declines in the same proportion, and the
resulting frost is intense.

The albedoes of the Jovian Planets are very high, and their
greysphere (radiative equilibrium) temperatures are correspondingly low; but the observed radiometric temperatures decline
very slowly, more, it would seem, as a result of the albedo than
of the growing distance from the Sun. These temperatures are
substantially above even the subsolar temperatures, which
mark the theoretical maximum due to Solar energy alone. If
we take the greysphere temperature and compare it with the
radiometric temperature, Jupiter's own heat will excel that of

the incoming sunlight 5.4 times. Microwave measurements find
a similar situation on Saturn. If we now take the subsolar
temperatures and compare these with the radiometric figures,
we find that Saturn's own radiation exceeds that received from
the Sun, when directly overhead, 3.7 times; the corresponding
figure for Uranus is 25 times and for Neptune 3.2 times. But
we must not jump to the conclusion that Saturn and Uranus
are intrinsically hotter than Jupiter: Saturn's share of Solar
energy is only a quarter that of Jupiter and is further pared by
a higher albedo, so that its thermal emission per unit surface
area is, in fact, less.

Uranus's high figure is due primarily to its high albedo:[211] it
is whiter than snow and retains only 7 per cent of the incident
Solar energy. This is about 12 times less than on Jupiter, so
that Uranus's thermal radiation is really below that of Saturn,
and Neptune's is still less. Kuiper thought that the radiometric
temperatures of all the Outer Planets bar Pluto were substantially the same: about 120°K, making them thermally
independent from the Sun.

The figures for surface gravity in Table III call for some
comment. The giant planets are very fast spinners, which in
globes of such dimensions causes a readily noticeable polar
flattening, or oblateness. The polar diameters of the four
Jovian planets are 134,000 (Jupiter), 107,700 (Saturn), 47,100
(Uranus) and 48,400km (Neptune).[212] The surface gravity is
higher at the poles and lower at the equator by reason of
oblateness alone, with a further decrease at the latter due to the
centrifugal force of rotation.

The actual gravity at Jupiter's equator is only 2.40g, but it
rises to 2.67g at the poles. The corresponding figures for
Saturn are 0.95 and 1.16g. The surface gravity at the equators
of Uranus and Neptune is similarly reduced to the substantially
terrestrial values of 1.05 and 1.18g^2. An Earthman would not
be unduly inconvenienced by *gravity* on any of the three
smaller Jovians.

The Coriolis force arises from the variation of the linear
speed of rotation with latitude (p 42). On an atmosphered and

cloudy planet it tends to produce alternating dark and bright belts, with descending and ascending currents corresponding to clearer and cloudier conditions respectively. The upper atmosphere of Venus is an example, but its speed of rotation is only a fraction that of the Jovians, where the belted atmospheric structure is strongly developed. Expectedly, it is most prominent on Jupiter, less so on Saturn and Uranus—although I have seen the latter display two strong dark *belts*. (The bright belts are known as *zones*.) Neptune is somewhat featureless, largely because of its great distance, which compounds a small apparent diameter with a low level of illumination. But faint belts have occasionally been seen there, too.

The Jovians may be thermally independent from the Sun, but it is doubtful if Pluto can have any appreciable heat of its own: it must be affected by the peculiar orientation of its polar axis, which is similar to that of Uranus.[213] The latter lies more or less prone in its orbital plane, spinning backwards, like Venus, about an axis inclined at 7° 53′ to it. As a result now the one, now the other pole faces the Sun during the solsticial quarters of its 85-year-long journey round the Sun; on Pluto, with a 'year' equal to 247 of ours, the effect is even more drastic. In addition, Pluto's highly-inclined and eccentric orbit brings it closer to the Sun than Neptune at perihelion and makes it recede to nearly 50AU into the outer murk at the other end. It is a most peculiar planet, and if Dirk Brouwer's estimate of its mass as 0.81 Earth-masses is correct it will have a mean density of about 20 and a surface gravity of $2g$.[214]

Table III lists only the largest 'planetary' satellites. The system of Jupiter, however, extends over nearly 50 million km and contains nine more satellites, most of which seem to be captured asteroids with diameters of about 20km. The four outermost ones have retrograde orbits, strongly perturbed by the Sun.

Saturn has ten known satellites in the 100–1,000km class, and may be orbited by some smaller bodies still awaiting discovery. It is the only planet adorned with a wide set of rings.

Uranus's five satellites of comparable size are crowded tightly around the planet. They are assigned unlikely densities of between 4 and 6, and are probably less dense and larger in proportion.

In addition to the retrograde Triton, which has the distinction of by far the highest surface gravity and escape velocity in the whole satellite tribe, Neptune has a smaller companion, Nereid, some 300km in diameter. This claims another distinction: the most eccentric orbit, which resembles that of a comet. Any bodies of the size of Jupiter's minor attendants would be invisible and the distance of Neptune.

Pluto seems to be a loner.

Jupiter: its appearance and atmosphere

Jupiter's surface detail is clearly atmospheric. Its bright zones and dark belts are well known to telescopic observers and correspond to ascending and descending atmospheric currents respectively. In the telescope the zones usually appear creamy-white, but occasionally (as happened during the summer and autumn of 1962) the 20°-wide equatorial zone is overlaid by a cinnamon-coloured veil and the whole planet assumes a pinkish hue.[215] This effect has been seen on Saturn as well and is probably of volcanic origin—or is a solar flare a better analogy? In some colour photographs, however, the zones have a greyish-blue cast, which seems to have been confirmed by the *Pioneer* probes.

Pioneer 10 passed within 130,000km of Jupiter's cloud tops on 4 December 1973, after a voyage of 21 months, and flew successively past Io, Europa, Ganymede and Callisto at between 150,000–800,000km during the following 20 days, being occulted by Io on the way. It was moving substantially in the planet's equatorial plane. *Pioneer 11* made a closer approach of 41,600km on 2 December 1974 and its trajectory took it over both poles. The *Pioneer* pictures of the satellites are poor. The imaging is in colour, obtained by combining pictures taken through a red and a blue filter. Maximum resolution in the pictures of Jupiter was 50km, which is quite unattainable from Earth, as are the small-phase and polar aspects of the planet.[216]

The *Pioneer* views give the belts an unnaturally orange hue, varying 'from yellow and delicate gold to red and bronze'.[217] From this colouring it has been inferred that, while the zone clouds consist of crystals of frozen ammonia, the belts are still cloud—but of frozen ammonia hydrosulphide—organic compounds have previously been suggested. Polarimetry shows that the crystals in both are very small: a few tenths of a μm across. The belts lie about 20km below the zones, and are some 10°C warmer.

Temperature and pressure at the cloud tops are estimated at −120°C and 700mb respectively, the former dropping to −155°C at the 100-mb level. A haze of aerosols, including frozen ethane and acetylene, overlies the clouds. The atmosphere between the adjacent zones and belts may reach relative velocities of up to 600km per hour.

The whole equatorial zone moves 410km per hour faster than the neighbouring belts. The flow is oppositely directed on the two sides of a zone. This is partly a matter of altitude (as rotation speed increases with the distance from the planet's centre), and partly of Coriolis forces, creating shearing stresses and huge eddies where the air streams meet. These eddies may be thousands of km across and are clearly visible in *Pioneer* pictures, as are wisps, streaks, loops and arches of bright cloud stretching across the belts.

Telescopic observers have reported occasional spots of brilliant blue and green within the belts, but these are rare. Red spots, similar in character to the Great Red Spot (to be described shortly) but much smaller and of brief duration, have been photographed by the *Pioneers*. Much commoner are large white oval spots with dark edges, explained as descending currents around the rising air column in a convection cell, responsible for the central condensation. Such convection cells may reach diameters of 4,000km, and some spots have been observed to blow along at 500km per hour.

The whole atmospheric scene is one of great activity, and violent electric storms are expected. Thus Jupiter is well-named: Zeus the Thunderer indeed.

Zones and belts vary a good deal in width, position and number. The equatorial zone has often been seen split by a narrow dark line, tentatively explained as the shadow cast by a thin ring similar to the Crepe Ring of Saturn (p 164). The *Pioneers* have not confirmed this, but have found around Jupiter a 300-fold increase in interplanetary dust.[218] This forms an extensive disc of meteoric matter, analogous to the one round the Sun which is responsible for the Zodiacal Light. There is also a doughnut-like bulge of hydrogen extending into the satellite system to beyond the orbit of Io, in addition to the vast belts of trapped corpuscular radiation (of which more presently).[219]

Since Jupiter's climate is dominated by its own rather than the Sun's heat, no differences have been found in the temperature of the day and night hemispheres, nor between the northern and southern halves of the planet. But the equatorial region is a little warmer than the poles, in which the increase of gravity towards the latter may play a part.

Expectedly the rotation period differs when measured at different latitudes, being the shortest for the equatorial zone (which forms the 'System I' quoted in the tables). In the greyish-blue polar regions the rotation is too low for belts and zones to form and they are meteorologically quiescent, with scattered clouds and areas of featureless blue—open skies. The cloud ceiling is lower as well. It has been suggested that these regions might be more favourable to life than the boisterous tropics.

The Great Red Spot

The two most peculiar features of the Jovian face are the Great Red Spot and the Veil, also known as the 'South Tropical Disturbance'. The Spot sits, glaring like a baleful eye, in the South Tropical Belt, which also houses the Veil.

The Spot is a latitudinal oval with pointed tips. It measures 40,000km long and 12,000km wide, and has been a permanent feature of unchanged dimensions ever since it was first sighted in 1663. It keeps its mean position but seems to bob up and down, which alters its colour from brick-red to pink, and on some occasions it has been completely effaced, with only a kind of bay marking its location. The Spot also drifts from side to side, so that it is not firmly anchored, yet it appears to have internal coherence.

The *Pioneers* make the Spot stand about 10km proud of the cloud banks at the present epoch. It goes once round the planet in 9 hours 55 minutes 40 seconds, which is 1 second faster than 'System II', where it lies. The ensuing friction expresses itself in broad arcs of cloud around the Spot and a tail behind it. The Spot itself has a certain amount of structure, but its nature is conjectural. It has been suggested that it may be a permanent storm centre; it is not associated with any gravitational anomaly, but this only shows that the Spot is in isostasic equilibrium (p 29) with its surroundings. Thus it could be a kind of floating island in suspension according to its specific gravity.

The Veil is even odder: a ghostly, darkish area between two bright spots some 70,000km apart. It has a period of 9 hours 55 minutes 19.5 seconds and overtakes the Spot every two years or so, flowing past and round it at 26km per hour, to reform on the other side. This ruffles up the nearby zones and belts; the Spot is dragged bodily along by the Veil for a space and then subsides into its former lodgement.[220]

Atmospheres on the Outer Planets

Our knowledge of the composition, structure and relation of the atmosphere to the interior of Jupiter is still in a state of flux. The *Pioneers* recorded hydrogen and helium in the UV glow of Jupiter, the ratio of the two gases being 85 : 15.[221] The ordinary spectrum shows strong absorptions due to methane and ammonia, which correspond to 150m and 7m respectively of these gases at STP (p 37). Deuterium, ethane, acetylene, hydrogen cyanide, sodium, and (somewhat doubtfully) dinitrogen tetroxide have been identified at various times as minor atmospheric constituents.[222] Recently Harold Larson and collaborators at the University of Arizona have discovered during airborne IR observations emission lines of water at 5 μm from localised hot spots.[223] Hydrogen sulphide (H_2S) is suspected.

The other Jovians have very similar atmospheres of hydrogen and helium. Ammonia is progressively frozen out of the spectroscopically accessible atmosphere with increasing distance, while methane absorptions are intensified and correspond to 2,200 metres on Saturn, 3,500 metres on Uranus, and 3,700 metres on Neptune. Whether this represents a real increase in the proportion of methane or is due simply to our being able to see deeper into the atmosphere (no longer shielded by ammonia clouds), is an open question. The molecular 8,720Å band of hydrogen is strong in the spectra of Uranus and Neptune, but its companion at 8,166Å is suppressed by a neutral gas, expected to be helium;[224] so that the helium content seems to be higher than on Jupiter, as is possibly that of deuterium, which has been identified from Earth.

But it is always a mistake to assume, as is often done, that the composition of a planet's outer gaseous envelope is a sure guide to that of the interior.

Jupiter's magnetic field

Like that of the Earth, Jupiter's magnetic field interacts with the Solar Wind in a teardrop, or tadpole-like, pattern. The bow shock at the Sunward end was first encountered by the *Pioneers* at 71,600km, or about 108 Jupiter radii (R_j); the tail reaches out at least to the orbit of Saturn. The magnetic field proper, comprising the radiation belts, has an outer diameter of 200R_j and an inner 'hard core' of 40R_j. The magnetosphere is shaped like a discus pinched at the centre about the planet; it is offset relatively to the rotational axis, causing the magnetosphere to wobble as the planet revolves.[225] This wobble affects the 'Jovian Wind' of electrons streaming out of Jupiter's magnetic field, which was detected at 100 million km.

The dipole has the strength of 12 gauss at the north pole and

9 gauss at the south according to the *Pioneer 11* data, but the observations from the Earth put it higher, at 30 and 20 gauss respectively (the Earth's field is 0.3 to 0.6 gauss). Closer to the planet the field has a more complicated structure with eight poles, but the situation is not clearly understood.

The intensity of radiation in Jupiter's 'Van Allen belts' exceeds that of the Earth's 10^4–10^6 times, and the radiation dosage encountered by the *Pioneers* would have been lethal to a human crew. The apparatus, however, escaped serious damage.

The Galileans and their atmospheres

Jupiter has a multi-layered ionosphere about 1,000km deep, and so does Io, the innermost satellite. From Io's peak electron density of 6×10^4 per cm^3 a ground-level atmospheric density of 10^{10} to 10^{12} molecules per cubic centimetres is doubtfully inferred. Sodium emission has been observed on Io from Earth;[226] nitrogen, methane and ammonia are expected, and water, in the form of ice, present on the other Galileans as well as rock material. Io is also enveloped in a broad hydrogen halo, which extends over one-third of its orbit. Its gravity is much too low to retain hydrogen, and this halo is sustained by interaction with Jupiter's hydrogen ring. Io crosses Jupiter's magnetosphere at each revolution, giving rise to an electro-magnetic shock with the energy of several H-bombs. This causes the strong radio emission between 16–24Mc/sec (10–20 metres), long known to radio astronomers.[227] Intense auroral displays are suspected.

The other satellites are also sweeping up protons from Jupiter and thus acquire hydrogen haloes, which may be of some importance for the greenhouse effect at low temperatures. Unaccountably, Callisto has been found to radiate twice as much heat as it receives from the Sun;[228] and Jupiter's heat radiation may have to be considered in the climate of the innermost satellites.

It has long been evident that they must have some atmospheric cover. This much follows from their high albedoes, yellow-to-orange colouring and the marked variation in brightness at short-wavelength colour as they revolve about Jupiter. D L Harris explains this as alternate precipitation and vaporisation of some substance (most probably ammonia or methane) on their surfaces at the evening and morning terminator.[229] The frequent eclipses by Jupiter have a similar effect; when Io emerges from Jupiter's shadow it looks very bright and has the highest albedo in the Solar System.[230]

In 1963 the Crimean Astrophysical Observatory announced the discovery of unidentified absorptions in the spectra of Io, Europa and Ganymede. Star occultations indicate a ground pressure of about 1 millibar on Ganymede. Io and Europa often look banded in the telescope, and a north polar cap extending down to 30° of latitude has recently been observed on Europa at the Mauna Kea Observatory in Hawaii. *Pioneer 11* has recorded a small but well-defined snow cap at the south pole of Callisto,[231] whose variation in reflectivity with phase indicates a very rough surface. And polar caps have been reported on Ganymede by telescopic observers on several occasions.

Pioneer 10's picture of Ganymede is of poor quality and has a resolution of about 400km; but according to Tom Gehrels it shows a south polar *mare* and another central *mare*, 800km in diameter, as well as large craters and a bright north polar region.[232] Results from *Pioneer 11* have not been fully processed but a general resemblance to the Moon, or perhaps Mars—with *maria* and craters—has been confirmed.

Before leaving Jupiter's companion worlds, it may be observed that although their escape velocities are comparable to that from the Moon, they are so cold and relatively sheltered from the Solar Wind that this does not represent a serious threat to an atmosphere of heavy gases.

And we shall see presently that low temperatures need not necessarily preclude some form of life.

Possibility of life; internal structure

It is a mistake to assume that life is irrevocably committed to our type of organic chemistry, based on water as the vital solvent and carbon as the chain- and ring-building element. There is a wide range of water-like solvents with their own systems of bases and acids, which duplicate with minor variations the fundamental reactions of our aquo-chemistry within different temperature ranges.

It is the freezing of water and the reduced reactivity of water-based radicals that form the main obstacle to life at low temperatures.[233] There are, however, several excellent water-like solvents with low freezing points. Ammonia freezes at $-77.7°C$, hydrogen sulphide at $-85.6°C$, methylamine at $-92.5°C$. All of these exist on the Jovian worlds, and alternative biochemistries can be worked out on their basis without much difficulty.[234] Difluoride oxide (F_2O), with a freezing point as low as $-224°C$ ($49°K$), presents many analogies to water and forms sufficiently unstable compounds with noble gases for a plausible cryo-biological system that could be viable even on Pluto.

On the other hand, we will recall (p 44) that organic compounds, including amino acids and nucleic acids, arise spontaneously in quasi-Jovian atmospheres under the action of UV radiation, electric discharge, radioactivity, and even simple heat. In other words, the prerequisites of life, possibly in several forms, exist on an enormous scale on the Jovian planets, and perhaps on some of their satellites. The fact that their conditions correspond in some ways to those of the primitive Earth does not mean that life on the Jovians, with several aeons of evolution behind it, must have remained at the same primitive stage.

The greatest snag is the internal structure of the Jovian planets and the possible absence of a solid surface.

Some years ago, models of Jupiter were in vogue where vast layers of ice, liquid and metallic hydrogen enveloped a quasi-terrestrial core.[235] This concept, however, requires low internal temperatures and cannot be sustained in the face of the substantial heat radiated by Jupiter. Venus, whose surface temperature is supposed to be 800°K, does not radiate any heat beyond what can be expected of its radiative equilibrium with the Solar input. But the Jovian planets do, and they certainly have more extensive cloudy atmospheres than Venus. A model which is a kind of compromise between the old ideas and the new is illustrated in Fig 6.[236] R Jastrow and S I Rasool propose a similar structure with a temperature of 500,000°C at the centre of the nife core; others have put it lower—at about 50,000°C. However, as the Earth's central temperature is in dispute, no great weight need be attached to such figures. Like many compromises, this one seems to fall between two stools and its approach remains basically terrestrial and planetary; and I think that the situation must be interpreted in stellar terms.

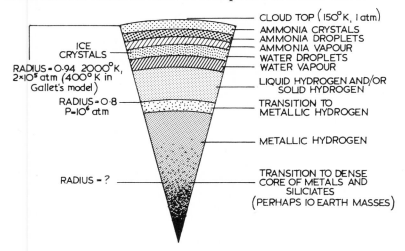

Fig 6 Model of Jupiter, after G Hunt (*New Scientist*)

The basic difference between a planet and a star is that the heat in the former is generated by atomic fission and in the latter by *fusion*. There may be transitional cases where both processes are at work simultaneously; but fusion is by far the greatest source of energy, and the pressure of the radiation it produces acts against gravitational compression, making for a low density regardless of the chemical make-up. Even in the Jastrow-Rasool quasi-planetary model the pressure of radiation cannot be neglected. The *Pioneer* data yield a temperature gradient of 2.3°C/km in the uppermost 80km of the Jovian atmosphere, which is an almost pure mixture of hydrogen and helium. This is very close to the theoretical adiabatic lapse for such composition. The pressure at the bottom of this layer is only about 100mb. At the level of 1,000mb the temperature is put at 250 + 30°K, and there is talk of transition from gas to liquid 1,000km deeper in. But at a depth of 3,000km the temperature is estimated at 7,000°K—some 1,000°C above that of the surface of the Sun—with a corresponding density of 0.23. This puts paid to the conception of Jupiter as a 'spinning ball of liquid hydrogen', and at one remove to the idea of its internal heat being generated by continued contraction.

The planetary models will not do: Jupiter is a 'potted star'.[237]

It will be recalled from p 13 that mass and size for a given density sets a limit to luminous stardom. Smaller bodies cool too rapidly and are soon snuffed out. But the governing assumption is that the heat is radiated off to space without let or hindrance, which is manifestly untrue. Cool stars are enveloped in a thickening smoke of metal oxides, carbides, nitrides and other refractory compounds; and, as their size continues to decrease, a point will be reached where this smoke forms an opaque envelope, doubly compressed by the pressure of radiation from within and of gravitation from without. But this cannot cause a drop in internal temperature; on the contrary, it will rise, as the escape of energy is effectively blocked. A nuclear 'engine' once started will go on.

Now even the lowest assumed temperatures of Jupiter's interior are adequate for initiating nuclear fusion. There is deuterium in the Jovian atmospheres, and the reaction $D_3 + H_1 = He_3 + \gamma$; $He_3 + He_3 = He_4 + 2H$ starts at 50,000°K. Lithium and beryllium 'burning' soon follow. In the case of Jupiter, and possibly Saturn, this could raise the central temperature to 1,000,000°C, required for the proton-

proton reaction, which is the main source of power in the Sun.
The question is, can any life survive in such conditions?

For one thing, the pressures in Jupiter's atmosphere are so
high that it is soon compressed to the density of a liquid, and a
form of aerial plankton is conceivable, perhaps stratified
according to its own and ambient composition and temperature.
For another, local hot spots (flares) may form beneath the
opaque envelope and occasionally break through in a great
eruption, vast amounts of incandescent gas pouring out·into
the overlaying cooler regions. This gas may be largely hydrogen,
but the envelope is of substantially rock-like composition and
will be shifted by the eruption. The mean densities of Io and
Europa indicate a make-up similar to that of Mars or the
Moon, which shows a considerable abundance of rock-forming
matter in the central region of proto-Jupiter (p 20).

The erupting mass may therefore be compared to a laccolith
and may eventually set into a kind of floating island at a level
corresponding to its specific gravity. The Great Red Spot may
be a case in point, and it is quite cold. Smaller, denser islands
will keep lower stations; the two small red spots observed by
Pioneer 10 were no longer there at the flyby of *Pioneer 11*. They
are of planetary dimensions, and could provide a foothold for
life.[238] Thus Jupiter could be a world of worlds.

Uranus and Neptune are smaller, denser and cooler. Here
the envelope. may have condensed into something like the
Earth's crust, overspread with a vast ocean of water or liquid
ammonia—we do not know enough even for an inspired guess,
and must keep our minds open.

Saturn

Without the rings, Saturn is a smaller, paler version of Jupiter.
It, too, has a broad equatorial zone which is often orange or
pinkish, and a set of greyish, more regular belts, nothing like
so dark as those of Jupiter. The equatorial zone, on the other
hand, is much brighter than the rest of the disc, which darkens
perceptibly towards the poles. Well-defined spots, usually

bright, are rare, and there are no permanent surface features comparable to the Great Red Spot or the Veil. To some extent this is a matter of distance: if Saturn could be put into Jupiter's place, some of the differences would be toned down.

Yet these differences have a substantive basis. With a smaller mass, Saturn's gravity is less than half Jupiter's, and its mean density of 0.706 is the lowest known in the Solar System. Thus, although the rotational centrifugal forces are much greater on Jupiter, Saturn's oblateness or flattening is higher: its polar diameter is 1/12 shorter than the equatorial. This indicates a marked concentration of mass towards the centre of the planet —which is only to be expected, for with so low a density most of Saturn's volume must be gaseous.

Since the radiometric temperature exceeds the greysphere one (Table III), it has been obvious for many years that Saturn is heated from within. In 1962 E J Öpik calculated that Saturn's internal heat escapes at the surface at the rate of 4.0×10^3 erg/cm^2/sec;[239] Saturn therefore radiates more heat than it could possibly receive from the Sun, and when the albedo is taken into consideration Öpik's figure is 2.87 times the Solar input.

In 1970 and 1971 J Condon, D Jancey and M Yarbury[240] measured the microwave emission of Saturn at 50 and 100cm with the 1,000-foot Arecibo radio-telescope and obtained brightness temperatures of $+115°C$ ($388°K$) and $+270°C$ ($543°K$) respectively. Saturn's adiabatic lapse is about $1.6°C/km$ so that such temperatures will be found much lower down than in Jupiter.[241] Nevertheless, it seems that Saturn is powered by substantially the same nuclear processes as Jupiter, and is 'inflated' to its low density by a comparable pressure of radiation acting against lower gravity. By the time the planet's mass has dropped to that of Neptune different reactions come into prominence and the density increases, although this may be due in whole or in part to intrinsic differences in chemical make-up.

Saturn's microwave emission is weakly polarised in the equatorial plane, which indicates a magnetic field. There must also be belts of trapped radiation, although nothing like as wide or intense as Jupiter's. According to T R McDonough and N M Brice of Cornell University, Saturn, like Jupiter, is surrounded by a doughnut-shaped ring of diffuse hydrogen extending beyond the orbit of Titan.

But the chief interest and attraction of Saturn lies in its much more material and obvious rings. Four of these are usually distinguished and marked A-D from the outside inwards.

The outermost Ring A (external diameter 239,600km) is separated at 239,600km by Cassini's Division from Ring B, which is the brightest of the four and bounded by diameters of 234,000 and 181,000km. There is no clear gap between it and the Crepe Ring C, with an inner diameter of 149,300. This ring is dark and less substantial than the previous two, the ball of Saturn being clearly visible through it. The Inner Crepe Ring, or Ring D, was discovered photographically at the Pic-du-Midi Observatory (France) in 1970; it too is dusky and even more diaphanous than Ring C. There also seems to be an attenuated halo in the outward extension of Ring A.

Cassini's Division (which owes its existence to synchronised perturbations by the innermost satellites) can be seen easily with a moderate telescope. But there are several other, narrower gaps, the most important of which is Encke's Division 4,850km from the outside edge of Ring A, inwards of which the ring is brighter.

The spectroscope shows that the speed of rotation of the rings increases towards Saturn in accordance with Kepler's laws, so that the rings consist of swarms of discrete bodies pursuing independent orbits. The density and composition of the swarms appear to vary, as probably does the size of the elements in them. Bright stars and Saturn's own satellites do not vanish when occulted by the rings but continue to shine through in diminished lustre, brightening up now and again as they en-counter a gap. Nevertheless, the rings are quite substantial: except for the innermost Crepe Rings they cast a dark shadow on the ball of the planet. Their thickness does not appear to exceed 65km and may average as low as 10km.

In 1958 Cook and Franklin studied the transmission of light

by the rings and detected the presence of a 'neutral gas' in the plane of Ring C. In 1969 Kuiper obtained IR spectra of the rings, showing absorptions of water ice. Ammonia snow has likewise been invoked to explain the brightness of the central rings. It was therefore believed that the rings might consist of a kind of giant hail—but they give a surprisingly strong radar echo, indicating a rocky composition. At 12.6cm they reflect better than Mercury and about 8 times as strongly as Mars, whereas R M Goldstein and G A Morris could detect no echo at all from the ball of Saturn at the NASA Goldstone satellite tracking station.[242]

This implies that the rings consist of rough boulders, metre-sized or larger. The existence of a thinner 'flying scree' outside Ring A is consistent with the radar results. IR spectra give a mean reflecting particle size of $25–125\,\mu m$, although this is ascribed to ices and silicates in the 'surface microstructure of the boulders'. Radio data suggest a 'population of particles' of centimetre diameters.

As they fall within the expected Van Allen belts, the rings would be magnetised and electrified. From polarimetric data Dollfus infers that the boulders are aligned with their long axes pointing at Saturn, which may be due to this. In any event the presence of heavy rock-forming materials at this distance from the planet's surface could be interpreted as a sign of a hard crust somewhere far below the clouds of Saturn itself. H Struve's estimate of the mass of the rings as 1/27,000th of Saturn's may have to be revised upwards, and they may have an appreciable gravitational field of their own.[243]

Titan, the third and largest satellite of Saturn, is a very intriguing body that warrants a closer look. The Table III data are burdened with considerable uncertainties, and in the light of the upward revision of the masses of Jupiter's Galilean satellites it seems likely that Titan, too, will prove somewhat more massive. On the present reckoning, Titan's escape velocity is about 2.75km/sec, not much above the Moon's. But its great distance from the Sun enables it to retain a substantial atmosphere. This shows absorptions of methane (corresponding to 210 metre-atmospheres[2]) and of hydrogen, a light gas which it would be unable to retain if not immersed in Saturn's hydrogen ring. Titan's atmosphere may contain other gases, but hydrogen is important as it alone can cause an appreciable greenhouse effect at Titan's low temperature. That this effect is present is borne out by microwave brightness temperatures, which rise from $93°K$ at $20\,\mu m$ to $146°K$ at $8.4\,\mu m$. According to one model the surface temperature would be about $155°K$ with a barometric pressure of 440mb. With a surface gravity of only $0.17g$, this would make Titan's atmosphere more massive than ours.[244] The visible surface is mainly cloud, and shares an orange tint with Jupiter's Io and Saturn's equatorial zone. But there is little more beyond doubtful laboratory hypotheses to go by; we have to wait and see.

Neptune's satellite Triton is placed even better to retain a massive atmosphere, and both could provide a home for some form of cold non-aqueous life.

Probing the Outer Planets

Pioneer 10 will reach Saturn's orbit in 1976, but will not find the planet there. *Pioneer 11* is again mainly a Jupiter probe with Saturn as an afterthought. But, having escaped damage in the swift flight through Jupiter's radiation belts, and been given a strong gravitational boost, it is now on the way to Saturn in working order, in a long Hohmann transfer which takes it to the other side of the Sun. *Pioneer 11* is not expected to reach Saturn until 2 or 3 September 1979, passing between the globe and the innermost ring at 1.05–1.15 Saturn radii from the planet's centre.

If this fails we shall have to wait for the two *Mariners*, scheduled for launch on 19 August and 17 September 1977 on a Jupiter/Saturn mission, reaching Jupiter in the spring of 1979 and Saturn in 1981. A Uranus probe is under consideration.

TABLE III

THE OUTER PLANETS AND THEIR 'PLANETARY' SATELLITES—PRINCIPAL DATA

Density is measured in g/cm³; *escape velocity* in km per sec; *Solar Flux at orbit* in Solar Constants; *sunlight* in mean full Moons. Bracketed figures for *albedo* are taken from the 9th edn of *The Smithsonian Physical Tables* (1954)

Jupiter
Mean distance from Sun: 5.203AU; *Orbital eccentricity:* 0.485; *Orbital inclination:* 1° 18′ 16.4″; *Orbital period:* 11.87 years; *Axial inclination:* 3° 04′; *Axial period:* 9 hrs 50 mins 30 secs; *Equatorial diameter:* 143,200km; *Mass:* 317.89; *Density:* 1.330; *Surface gravity:* 2.64g; *Escape velocity:* 60.22; *Solar Flux at orbit:* 0.04; *Mean apparent diameter of Sun:* 6′ 09″; *Sunlight:* 16,440; *Greysphere temp:* 88.5°K; *Subsolar temp:* 125°K; *Radiometric temp:* 135°K; *Albedo:* 0.73 (0.51)

Io (JI)
Mean distance from primary: 0.00121AU; *Orbital eccentricity:* 0.000; *Orbital inclination:* 0; *Orbital period:* 1.769 days; *Axial inclination:* ?; *Axial period:* 1.769 days; *Equatorial diameter:* 3,660km; *Mass:* 0.0150; *Density:* 3.5; *Surface gravity:* 0.182g⊙; *Escape velocity:* 2.55; *Solar Flux at orbit:* 0.04; *Mean apparent diameter of Sun:* 6′ 09″; *Sunlight:* 16,440; *Greysphere temp:* 101°K; *Subsolar temp:* 142°K; *Radiometric temp:* 110°K; *Albedo:* 0.60 (0.54)

Europa (JII)
Mean distance from primary: 0.00449AU; *Orbital eccentricity:* 0.0001; *Orbital inclination:* 0.5°; *Orbital period:* 3.551 days; *Axial inclination:* ?; *Axial period:* 3.551 days; *Equatorial diameter:* 2,960km; *Mass:* 0.0081²⁴⁵; *Density:* 3.4; *Surface gravity:* 0.143g⊙; *Escape velocity:* 2.03; *Solar Flux at orbit:* 0.04; *Mean apparent diameter of Sun:* 6′ 09″; *Sunlight:* 16,440; *Greysphere temp:* 103°K; *Subsolar temp:* 146°K; *Radiometric temp:* ?; *Albedo:* 0.70 (0.49)

Ganymede (JIII)
Mean distance from primary: 0.0072AU; *Orbital eccentricity:* 0.0014; *Orbital inclination:* 0.2°; *Orbital period:* 7.155 days; *Axial inclination:* ?; *Axial period:* 7.155 days; *Equatorial diameter:*

5,200km; *Mass:* 0.0249[245]; *Density:* 1.8; *Surface gravity:* 0.133g☉; *Escape velocity:* 2.60; *Solar Flux at orbit:* 0.04; *Mean apparent diameter of Sun:* 6′ 09″; *Sunlight:* 16,440; *Greysphere temp:* 112°K; *Subsolar temp:* 158°K; *Radiometric temp:* 126°K; *Albedo:* 0.40 (0.29)

Callisto (JIV)

Mean distance from primary: 0.0126AU; *Orbital eccentricity:* 0.0074; *Orbital inclination:* 0.2°; *Orbital period:* 16.689 days; *Axial inclination:?*; *Axial period:* 16,689 days; *Equatorial diameter:* 4,720km; *Mass:* 0.0178[245]; *Density:* 1.5; *Surface gravity:* 0.132g☉; *Escape velocity:* 2.47; *Solar Flux at orbit:* 0.04; *Mean apparent diameter of Sun:* 6′ 09″; *Sunlight:* 16,440; *Greysphere temp:* 117°K; *Subsolar temp:* 166°K; *Radiometric temp:* ?; *Albedo:* 0.20 (0.15)

Saturn

Mean distance from Sun: 9.539AU; *Orbital eccentricity:* 0.056; *Orbital inclination:* 2° 29′ 21.8″; *Orbital period:* 29.42 years; *Axial inclination:* 26° 44′; *Axial period:* 10 hrs 14 mins; *Equatorial diameter:* 119,300km; *Mass:* 95.17; *Density:* 0.706; *Surface gravity:* 1.16g; *Escape velocity:* 36.26; *Solar Flux at orbit:* 0.01; *Mean apparent diameter of Sun:* 3′ 22″; *Sunlight:* 4,365; *Greysphere temp:* 63.4°K; *Subsolar temp:* 90°K; *Radiometric temp:* 125°K; *Albedo:* 0.76 (0.50)

Titan (SVI)

Mean distance from primary: 0.00816AU; *Orbital eccentricity:* 0.029; *Orbital inclination:* 0.3°; *Orbital period:* 15.945 days; *Axial inclination:* ?; *Axial period:* 15.945 days; *Equatorial diameter:* 4,800km; *Mass:* 0.023; *Density:* 2.3; *Surface gravity:* 0.17g; *Escape velocity:* 2.75; *Solar Flux at orbit:* 0.01; *Mean apparent diameter of Sun:* 3′ 22″; *Sunlight:* 4,365; *Greysphere temp:* 87.2°K; *Subsolar temp:* 123°K; *Radiometric temp:* 146°K; *Albedo:* 0.12

Uranus

Mean distance from Sun: 19.182AU; *Orbital eccentricity:* 0.047; *Orbital inclination:* 0° 46′ 23.3″; *Orbital period:* 84.61 years; *Axial inclination:* 97° 53′; *Axial period:* 10 hrs 49 mins; *Equatorial diameter:* 22,800; *Mass:* 14.6; *Density:* 1.71; *Surface gravity:* 1.11g; *Escape velocity:* 22.5; *Solar Flux at orbit:* 0.003; *Mean apparent diameter of Sun:* 1′ 41″; *Sunlight:* 1,318; *Greysphere temp:* 32.7°K; *Subsolar temp:* 46°K; *Radiometric temp:* 103°K; *Albedo:* 0.93 (0.66)

Neptune

Mean distance from Sun: 30.058AU; *Orbital eccentricity:* 0.009; *Orbital inclination:* 1° 46′ 20.8″; *Orbital period:* 165.2 years; *Axial inclination:* 28° 48′; *Axial period:* 15 hrs 48 mins; *Equatorial diameter:* 19,300; *Mass:* 17.2; *Density:* 1.77; *Surface gravity:* 1.2g; *Escape velocity:* 23.9; *Solar Flux at orbit:* 0.001; *Mean apparent diameter of Sun:* 1′ 04″; *Sunlight:* 436; *Greysphere temp:* 57.4°K; *Subsolar temp:* 81°K; *Radiometric temp:* 108°K; *Albedo:* 0.84 (0.62)

Triton (NI)

Mean distance from primary: 0.0024AU; *Orbital eccentricity:* 0; *Orbital inclination:* 159.9°; *Orbital period:* 5.877 days; *Axial inclination:* ?; *Axial period:* 5.877 days; *Equatorial diameter:* 3,700 (5,700)km; *Mass:* 0.0344^{245}; *Density:* 5.1?; *Surface gravity:* 0.27g; *Escape velocity:* 3.13 (4.8?); *Solar Flux at orbit:* 0.001; *Mean apparent diameter of Sun:* 1′ 04″; *Sunlight:* 436; *Greysphere temp:* ?; *Subsolar temp:* ?; *Radiometric temp:* ?; *Albedo:* (0.21)

Pluto

Mean distance from Sun: 39.242AU; *Orbital eccentricity:* 0.2476; *Orbital inclination:* 17° 15′; *Orbital period:* 247.0 years; *Axial inclination:* 90°?; *Axial period:* 6.417 days; *Equatorial diameter:* 5,900km?; *Earth mass:* 0.08?; *Density:* 4.5?; *Surface gravity:* 0.43g?; *Escape velocity:* 4.2?; *Solar Flux at orbit:* 6 × 10^{-5}; *Mean apparent diameter of Sun:* 49″; *Sunlight:* 251; *Greysphere temp:* 42°K; *Subsolar temp:* 59°K; *Radiometric temp:* ?; *Albedo:* 0.14

The Moon (for comparison)

Mean distance from Sun: 0.00257AU; *Orbital eccentricity:* 0.549; *Orbital inclination:* 23.4°; *Orbital period:* 27.322 days; *Axial inclination:* 1° 32′; *Axial period:* 27.322 days; *Equatorial diameter:* 3,476km; *Earth mass:* 0.0123; *Density:* 3.34; *Surface gravity:* 0.16g; *Escape velocity:* 2.38; *Solar Flux at orbit:* 1.000; *Mean apparent diameter of Sun:* 31′ 59″; *Sunlight:* 436,500; *Greysphere temp:* 273°K; *Subsolar temp:* 385°K; *Albedo:* 0.07 (0.072)

Notes to Chapters and Further Reading

1 Between the old and the new

1 Ericke, Krafft A, *Space Flight*, Vol, II. Van Nostrand, London (1962)
2 Firsoff, V A, *Exploring the Planets.* A S Barnes, Cranbury NJ and New York (1968)
3 Waller, Peter, 'Pioneer 11 to be retargeted', *NASA News*, Release 74–10 (19.3.1974)
4 Bodechtel, Johann, and Gierloff-Emden, H C, *The Earth from Space.* David & Charles, Newton Abbot, Devon (1974)
5 Lovelock, James, and Epton, Sidney, 'The Quest for Gaia', *New Scientist*, 65 (935,) pp 304ff (1975)

2 Planets, planetary systems and sub-systems

6 Kuiper, G P, *Procs. of the National Academy of Sciences*, 40, pp 1069ff (1954)
7 Allen, C W, *Astrophysical Quantities.* University of London Press (1963 and 1973)
8 Firsoff, V A, *Facing the Universe.* A S Barnes, Cranbury NJ and New York (1968)
9 Ibid; *see also* Firsoff, V A, *Life Among the Stars.* Wingate, London (1974)
10 British Astronomical Association, *Handbook 1974*
11 Dauvillier, A, *L'Origine des Planètes.* Presses Universitaires de France, Paris (1956)
12 Singer, S F, *Irish Astronomical Jrnl.*, 4 (6) (1967); and Hindley, Keith, 'The Debris', *The Solar System* (*New Scientist* Special Review, 1975)
13 Firsoff, V A, *Strange World of the Moon.* Hutchinson, London (1959)

14 Dauvillier, A, *L'Origine des Planètes*; Dingle, Herbert, *Endeavour*, 17, pp 129ff (1958); Jones, Sir Spencer, *Endeavour*, 17, pp 140ff (1958); Russell, H N, *The Solar System and its Origin*. Macmillan, New York (1935)

15 Hoyle, Fred, 'The Origin of the Solar Nebula', *Quarterly Journal of the RAS*, 1 (28), (1960)

16 Kuiper, G P, and Middlehurst, Barbara, *Planets and Satellites, The Solar System, III*. University of Chicago Press (1961)

17 Alfvén, Hannes, 'On the Origin of the Solar System', *New Scientist*, 7, pp 1182ff (1960)

18 Hoyle, Fred, *op. cit.*

19 Dauvillier, A, *L'Origine des Planètes*; *see also Cosmologie et Chimie* (Presses Universitaires de France, Paris (1955)

20 *New Scientist*, 63 (916), p 783 (1974)

21 Kumar, S S, 'Planetary Systems' in *The Emerging Universe* (eds Saslaw, W, and Jacobs, K). University Press of Virginia (preprint, 1972)

22 *Science Horizons*, 133, p 14 (1972)

23 Oparine, A, and Fessenkov, V, *La Vie dans l'Univers*. Editions en Langues Etrangères, Moscow (1958)

24 Firsoff, V A, *Facing the Universe* and *Life Among the Stars*

25 British Astronomical Association, *Handbook 1960*; Dauvillier, A, *L'Origine des Planètes*

26 Williams, I P, *The Observatory*, 93, p 221 (1973)

27 *Astronomical Journal*, 78, p 1104 (1974)

28 Firsoff, V A, *Facing the Universe*; Oparine & Fessenkov, *La Vie dans l'Univers*

29 Sagan, Carl, and Page, Thornton (eds), *UFO's—A Scientific Debate*. Cornell University Press, Ithaca and London (1972)

3   The third Solar Planet

30 Holmes, Arthur, *Principles of Physical Geology*. Nelson, London and Edinburgh (1965)

31 Crawford, A R, *Nature*, 197, p 140 (1963)

32 Elston, W E, *Annals of the New York Academy of Sciences,* 123, p 817 (1965)

33 Kloosterman, J B, *Giant Ring Volcanoes on the Guiana Shield* (preprint, 1973)

34 Gass, I G et al, *Understanding the Earth*. 2nd Edn, The Artemis Press (1973)

35 Brooks, C E P, *Climate through the Ages*. Benn, London (1950)

36 Holmes, Arthur, *Principles of Physical Geology*
37 Jeffreys, Sir Harold, *The Earth.* Cambridge University Press (1953)
38 Jeans, Sir James, *The Dynamic Theory of Gases.* Cambridge University Press (1925)
39 Firsoff, V A, *The Old Moon and the New.* A S Barnes, Cranbury NJ and New York (1970); Ziering, Sigi, and Hu, Pung Nien, *Astronautica Acta*, 13, pp 327ff (1967)
40 Firsoff, V A, *Science*, 131, pp 1, 669ff (1960)
41 Humphreys, W J, *Physics of the Air.* McGraw-Hill, New York and London (1940)
42 Firsoff, V A, *Life Beyond the Earth.* Hutchinson, London; Basic Books, New York (1963); Wexler, Harry, in *Climatic Change*, Shapley, H *et al*, pp 173ff, Harvard University Press (1953)
43 Brooks, C E P, *op. cit.*
44 Monod, Jacques, *Chance and Necessity.* Collins, London (1972)
45 Firsoff, V A, *Life Beyond the Earth*; Oparin, A I, *Life: Its Nature, Origin and Development.* Oliver & Boyd, Edinburgh (1961)
46 Firsoff, V A, *Life Among the Stars*; Monod, Jacques, *op. cit.*
47 Firsoff, V A, *Life Beyond the Earth*
48 Bodechtel and Gierloff-Emden, *op. cit.*; USIS (US Information Service), *Science Horizons*, 134, pp 15ff (May 1972)
49 USIS and Zeiss, *The Great Project* (1971) and *Calendar 1973*
50 USIS; *Science Horizons*, 124, pp 3ff (May 1971)
51 Zeiss and USIS, *Calendar 1973*
52 Bodechtel and Gierloff-Emden, *op. cit.*; USIS and Zeiss, *The Great Project* (1971); and *Calendar 1973*

4   The Moon

53 Jeffreys, Sir Harold, *op. cit.*; Runcorn, S K, 'Lunar Dust', *Science Journal*, 6, pp 27ff (1970); Wood, J A *et al*, *Mineralogy and Petrology of the Apollo 12 Lunar Sample.* Smithsonian Astrophysical Observatory, Special Report 333 (20.5.1971)
54 Firsoff, V A, *The Old Moon and the New*; Kopal, Zdeněk, *Exploration of the Moon by Spacecraft.* Oliver & Boyd, Edinburgh and London (1968)
55 Kopal, Zdeněk, *op. cit.*
56 Gass, I G *et al*, *op. cit.*
57 Firsoff, V A, *The Old Moon and the New*
58 Geake, J E, 'The Physics of Lunar and Planetary Surfaces', *Contemporary Physics*, 15 (2), pp 121ff (1974)

59 Page, T L, 'Notes on the 4th Lunar Science Congress—II,' *Sky and Telescope*, 46 (1), pp 14ff (1973)
60 Firsoff, V A, *The Old Moon and the New*
61 Page, T L, *op. cit.*
62 Wood, J A *et al*, *op. cit.*
63 Bülow, Kurd von *et al*, *Eclogae Geologicae Helvetiae*, 56, pp 853ff (1963)
64 Gass, I G *et al*, *op. cit.*
65 Bülow, Kurd von *et al*, *op. cit.*; Fielder, Gilbert, *Lunar Geology*. Lutterworth Press (London 1965); Firsoff, V A, *The Old Moon and the New*; Moore, P, and Cattermole, P, *The Craters of the Moon*, Lutterworth Press (London 1967)
66 Spurr, J E, *The Shrunken Moon*. Business Press (1949)
67 Firsoff, V A, *Jrnl of the British Astr Assn*, 77, pp 251ff (1967)
68 Firsoff, V A, *Surface of the Moon*. Hutchinson (London 1961)
69 Fielder, Gilbert, *op. cit.*; and 'Lunar Igneous Activity and Differentiation', *Highlights of Astronomy*, Vol II, pp 142ff. Reidel (Dordrecht 1971); Firsoff, V A, *The Old Moon and the New*
70 Fielder, Gilbert, *Contemporary Physics*, 14, pp 39ff (1973)
71 Firsoff, V A, *Surface of the Moon*
72 Kloostermann, J B, *op. cit.*; Holmes, Arthur, *op. cit.*
73 Cameron, Winifred S, *Icarus*, 16, pp 339ff (1972); Firsoff, V A, *The Old Moon and the New*
74 Page, T L, *op. cit.*
75 Page, T L, *op. cit.*
76 Runcorn, S K, *op. cit.*; *Science*, 'The Moon Issue', 167 (1970); Wood, J A *et al*, *op. cit.*
77 Spurr, J E, *op. cit.*
78 Kuiper, G P, *op. cit.*
79 *New Scientist*, 53, pp 310ff (1972)
80 Cameron, Winifred S, *op. cit.*
81 Gurshtein, Alexander, *New Scientist*, 61, p 190f (1974)
82 Firsoff, V A, *Science*, 130, pp 1, 337f (1959); *Science*, 131, pp 1, 669ff (1960)
83 Page, T L, 'Notes on the 4th Lunar Science Congress—III', *Sky and Telescope*, 46 (2), pp 88ff (1973)
84 Fielder, Gilbert, *Lunar Geology*; Firsoff, V A, *The Old Moon and the New*; Kopal, Zdeněk, *An Introduction to the Study of the Moon*. Reidel (Dordrecht 1966)
85 Page, T L, 'Notes on the 4th Lunar Science Congress—II'
86 de Sitter, L U, *Structural Geology*. McGraw-Hill (London 1956)
87 Fielder, Gilbert, *Lunar Geology*; Firsoff, V A, *The Old Moon and the New*; Moore, P, and Cattermole, P, *op. cit.*

88 USIS and Zeiss, *The Great Project* (1971)
89 Gold, Thomas, *Monthly Notices of the RAS*, 115 (6) (1955); USIS and Zeiss, *The Great Project*
90 Page, T L, 'Notes on the 4th Lunar Science Congress—II'
91 Gold, Thomas, *op. cit.*
92 Holmes, Arthur, *op. cit.*
93 de Sitter, L U, *op. cit.*
94 Firsoff, V A, *Jrnl of the British Astr Assn*, 66, pp 314ff (1956); ditto 67, pp 309ff (1957); *Surface of the Moon*; Fielder, Gilbert, *Lunar Geology*
95 Firsoff, V A, *Surface of the Moon*
96 Firsoff, V A, *The Old Moon and the New*
97 MacBain, J W, *The Sorption of Gases and Vapours by Solids*. Routledge & Kegan Paul (London 1932)
98 *New Scientist*, 53, pp 310ff (1972)
99 Firsoff, V A, *Jrnl of the British Astr Assn*, 77, pp 251ff (1967); *The Old Moon and the New*
100 Firsoff, V A, *The Old Moon and the New*; Page, T L, 'Noted on the 4th Lunar Science Congress—III'; *Science*, 'The Moon Issue' 167 (1970)
101 Runcorn, S K, *op. cit.*
102 Burlinghame, A L *et al*, *op. cit.*
103 Fielder, Gilbert, *Contemporary Physics*, 14, pp 39ff (1973)
104 Cameron, Winifred S, *Jrnl of Geophysical Research*, 69, pp 2, 423ff (1964)
105 Firsoff, V A, *The Old Moon and the New*
106 *New Scientist*, 55, p 127 (1972)
107 Wood, J A *et al*, *op. cit.*
108 Firsoff, V A, *The Old Moon and the New*

5   The Iron Planet

109 Firsoff, V A, *The Interior Planets*. Oliver & Boyd (Edinburgh and London, 1968)
110 Firsoff, V A, *The Interior Planets*. Oliver & Boyd (Edinburgh and London, 1968)
111 British Astronomical Association, *Handbook 1974*
112 Camichel, H, and Dollfus, A, 'Rotation and cartography of Mercury' (preprint, 1967)
113 Antoniadi, E M, *La Planète Mercure*. Gauthier-Villars (Paris 1934); *The Planet Mercury* (English translation by Patrick Moore). Reid (Shaldon, Devon, 1974)
114 Jet Propulsion Laboratory (JPL) *Mariner 10 Venus Encounter*

Press Kit (1973); JPL *Mariner Venus-Mercury 1973 Status Bulletin*, Nos 27 and 28 (1974)
115 JPL, *Mariner Venus-Mercury 1973 Status Bulletin*
116 Burgess, Eric, 'A Hat-Trick for Mariner', *New Scientist*, 65 (943), pp 15ff (1975)
117 JPL, *Mariner Venus-Mercury 1973 Status Bulletin*
118 Dollfus, Audoin, *Comptes Rendus de l'Acad. Sci.*, 234 (1952)
119 Antoniadi, E M, *The Planet Mercury*; Firsoff, V A, *The Interior Planets*
120 Firsoff, V A, *The Interior Planets*
121 Sandner, Werner, *The Planet Mercury*. Faber (London 1963)
122 *Soviet News*, 5728 (12.3.1974)
123 Antoniadi, E M, *op. cit.*
124 JPL, *Mariner Venus-Mercury 1973 Status Bulletin*
125 *New Scientist* (Mercury issue), 185 (4146), 1974
126 Burgess, Eric, *op. cit.*
127 *New Scientist* (Mercury issue)
128 *New Scientist* (Mercury issue)
129 NASA, *Mariner Venus-Mercury 1973 Status Bulletin*, Nos 35 and 36 (1974)
130 *New Scientist* (Mercury issue)
131 MacBain, J W, *op. cit.*
132 NASA, *Mariner Venus-Mercury 1973 Status Bulletin*; *New Scientist* (Mercury issue)

6   The improbable Venus

133 Firsoff, V A, *Our Neighbour Worlds*, Hutchinson, London (1952)
134 JPL, *Mariner Venus-Mercury 1973 Status Bulletin*, No 19, Part 2
135 Jeffreys, Sir Harold, *The Earth*
136 Lewis, J S, 'The chemistry of the Solar System', *Scientific American*, 230 (3), pp 50ff (1974)
137 Bottema, M *et al*, *Journal of Geophysical Research* (1.9.1965); Plummer, W T and Strong, J, *Astronautica Acta*, 2 (6), 1965
138 Goody, Richard, *New Scientist*, 58, pp 602ff (1973); JPL, *Mariner 10 Venus Encounter Press Kit* (1973)
139 *New Scientist*, 60 (876), p 751 (1973)
140 Firsoff, V A, *The Interior Planets*
141 Firsoff, V A, *The Interior Planets*
142 Firsoff, V A, 'Visual observation of the planets with colour filters', *Discovery*, pp 231ff (June 1961); *The Interior Planets*
143 Moore, Patrick, *The Planet Venus*, 3rd edn, Faber, London (1961)

144 Firsoff, V A, *The Interior Planets*
145 Firsoff, V A, 'Visual observation of the planets with colour filters'
146 Guinot, Bernard, *Comptes Rendues de l'Academie des Sciences*, Groupe 5, 260, pp 431ff (1965)
147 Firsoff, V A, *The Interior Planets*
148 Warner, Brian, *Mthly Notices of the RAS*, 121, pp 279ff (1960)
149 Firsoff, V A, *Life Among the Stars*; Hall, R W and Branson, N J B A, *Mthly Notices of the RAS*, 151, p 185 (1971)
150 Firsoff, V A, *Life Among the Stars* and *The Interior Planets*
151 Goody, Richard, *op. cit.*
152 JPL, *Mariner 10 Venus Encounter Press Kit* (1973)
153 JPL, *Mariner Venus-Mercury 1973 Status Bulletin*, No 19, Part 2 (7.2.1974)
154 JPL, *Mariner Venus-Mercury 1973 Status Bulletin*, No 19, Part 2 (7.2.1974)
155 Firsoff, V A, *Exploring the Planets* and *The Interior Planets*
156 *Cornell University Bulletin* (March 1973)
157 Hunt, Garry, 'Veneras 9 and 10 create a sensation', *New Scientist*, p 260 (30.10.1975)
158 *New Scientist*, Vol 71, 1007 (1.7.1976)
159 *New Scientist*, Vol 71, 1007 (1.7.1976)
160 Firsoff, V A, *Life Beyond the Earth* and *Life Among the Stars*
161 Hunt, Garry, 'Veneras 9 and 10 create a sensation'
162 Elson, B M, 'Pioneer Venus Flights planned for 1978', *Aviation Week and Space Technology* (18.2.1974)

7 Mars: a 'little Earth'?

163 Mamikunian, G and Briggs, M (eds), *Current Aspects of Exobiology*. Pergamon Press, Oxford (1965)
164 Lowell, Percival, *Mars as the Abode of Life*, New York (1909)
165 British Astronomical Association, Handbook 1974; JPL, *Mariner Mars 1971 Project Final Report. Technical Report 32–1550*, Vol IV (1973)
166 British Astronomical Association, Handbook 1974; JPL, *Mariner Mars 1971 Project Final Report. Technical Report 32–1550*, Vol IV (1973)
167 JPL, *Mariner Mars 1971 Project Final Report*. Steinbacher, R H, and Haynes, N R, *Icarus*, 18, pp 64ff (1973)
168 JPL, *Mariner Mars 1971 Project Final Report:* Moore, P and Cross, C A, *Mars*, Beazley, London (1973)
169 JPL, *Mariner Mars 1971 Project Final Report*
170 Firsoff, V A, *Exploring the Planets*

171 JPL, *Mariner Mars 1971 Project Final Report*
172 *New Scientist*, 59, 'Monitor' (19.7.1973)
173 Lowell, Percival, *op. cit.*
174 Richardson, R S, *Man and the Planets*, Muller, London (1954)
175(a) JPL, *Mariner Mars 1971 Project Final Report*
175(b) Novosti Information Service, *Bulletin*, No 14, 904 (19.3.1974), and No 14, 928 (26.3.1974)
176 Burgess, Eric, 'The first days on Mars', *New Scientist*, 71, pp 214ff (29.7.1976); *New Scientist*, 71, pp 476 and 480 (2.9.1976); *Sky and Telescope*, 52 (2), pp 92ff (August 1976)
177 USIS, *Backgrounder* (26.7.1976)
178 Miner, E D, private communication 2.7.1973
179 Burgess, Eric, 'The first days on Mars'; *Sky and Telescope*, 52 (3), pp 156ff and 171ff (September 1976)
180 Firsoff, V A, *The Observatory*, 93 pp 85ff (1973)
181 *Sky and Telescope*, 52 (3) pp 156ff and 171ff (September 1976)
182 Burgess, Eric, 'The first days on Mars'
183 *Sky and Telescope*, 52 (3) pp 156ff and 171ff (September 1976)
184 Firsoff, V A, 'Some Problems of the Martian Atmosphere' (communicated to JPL in August 1973)
185 JPL, *Mariner Mars 1971 Project Final Report* (1973)
186 NASA Viking Project, *Mission Status Bulletin*, No 29 (21.6.1976)
187 JPL, *Mariner Mars 1971 Project Final Report* (1973)
188 Driscoll, Everly, 'Heavy weather over Mars'—USIS *Feature*
189 JPL, *Mariner Mars 1971 Project Final Report* (1973)
190 Firsoff, V A, *The World of Mars*, Oliver & Boyd, Edinburgh and London (1968)
191 Capen, C F and Martin, L J, *Lowell Observatory Bulletin*, No 157, 7, p 211 (1971)
192 Slipher, E C, *Mars—The Photographic Study*, Pergamon Press, Oxford (1965)
193 Firsoff, V A, *Exploring the Planets* and *The World of Mars*
194 JPL, *Mariner Mars 1971 Project Final Report* (1973)
195 Sagan, Carl, *et al*, *Icarus*, 17 (2), pp 346ff (1972)
196 JPL, *Mariner Mars 1971 Project Final Report* (1973)
197 Mamikunian and Briggs, *op. cit.*
198 Sagan, Carl, *Icarus*, 15, pp 511ff (1971)
199 Novosti Information Service, *Bulletin*, No 14, 928 (26.3.1974)
200 Burgess, Eric, 'The first days on Mars'; *Science News*, 110, pp 4ff (3.7.1976)
201 Viking Press Kit, *NASA Release*, No 75–183
202 *Sky and Telescope*, 52 (3), pp 156ff and 171ff (September 1976)

203 Lewin, Roger, 'Life on Mars: Curiouser and Curiouser', *New Scientist*, 71, pp 328ff (12.8.1976); *New Scientist*, 71, pp 476 and 480 (2.9.1976); *New Scientist*, 71, p 439 (26.8.1976); USIS *Features*, 3.8.1976, 6.8.1976 and 27.8.1976

204 Lewin, Roger, 'Life on Mars: Curiouser and Curiouser'

205 *New Scientist*, 71, p 439 (26.8.1976)

206 *The Guardian*, 7.9.1976

207 *Science News*, 110, pp 4ff (3.7.1976)

208 *Sky and Telescope*, 52 (3), pp 156ff and 171ff (September 1976)

209 JPL, *Mariner Mars 1971 Project Final Report* (1973)

8 The Outer Planets

210 Firsoff, V A, *Exploring the Planets*

211 British Astronomical Association, *Handbook 1974*

212 British Astronomical Association, *Handbook 1974*

213 Andersson, Leif, *Sky and Telescope*, p 277 (May 1973); *Sky and Telescope*, 47 (4) 1974

214 Firsoff, V A, *Life Among the Stars*; Kuiper, G P and Middlehurst, Barbara, *Planets and Satellites, The Solar System, III*, University of Chicago Press (1961)

215 Firsoff, V A, *Exploring the Planets*

216 Hunt, Garry, *New Scientist*, 61, pp 125ff (1974); *Science*, 'Pioneer 10' (various authors), 183, pp 301ff (1974)

217 *NASA News*, 74–292 (19.11.1974)

218 NASA, *Educational Data Sheet* 713 (January 1974)

219 *Science*, 'Pioneer 10'

220 Firsoff, V A, *Exploring the Planets*; Kuiper, G P, and Middlehurst, Barbara, *Planets and Satellites, The Solar System, III*

221 *Science*, 'Pioneer 10'

222 Firsoff, V A, *Exploring the Planets*; Kuiper, G P, and Middlehurst, Barbara, *op. cit.*

223 *New Scientist*, 65 (940), p 620 (1975)

224 *Sky and Telescope*, 20, p 263 (1960)

225 Hunt, Garry, *New Scientist*, *op. cit.*; *Science*, 'Pioneer 10'

226 Brown, Robert, 'Io: Jupiter's surprising satellite', *New Scientist*, 65 (943), pp 15ff (1975)

227 Firsoff, V A, *Exploring the Planets*

228 Kuzmin, A D, and Losousky, B ya, *Icarus*, 18, p 222 (1973); *New Scientist*, p 200 (23.7.1964)

229 Firsoff, V A, *Exploring the Planets*; Kuiper, G P, and Middlehurst, Barbara, *op. cit.*

230 *NASA News*, 7–238 (10.9.1974)

231 USIS, 'The Triumph of Pioneer 11' (3.12.1974)
232 *NASA News*, 7–238 (10.9.1974)
233 Firsoff, V A, *Life Beyond the Earth* and *Life Among the Stars*
234 Firsoff, V A, *Life Beyond the Earth* and *Life Among the Stars*
235 Firsoff, V A, *Exploring the Planets*; Kuiper, G P, and Middle-
     hurst, Barbara, *op. cit.*
236 Dalgarno, A, and McElroy, M B, *Science*, 170, p 167 (1970);
     Hunt, Garry, *New Scientist*, 61, pp 125ff (1974)
237 Firsoff, V A, *Our Neighbour Worlds*
238 Firsoff, V A, *Life Beyond the Earth* and *Exploring the Planets*
239 Öpik, E. J, *Icarus*, 1 (3), pp 220ff (1962)
240 *New Scientist*, 61, p 118 (1974)
241 Firsoff, V A, *Exploring the Planets*
242 *New Scientist*, 61, p 118 (1974)
243 Kuiper, G P, and Middlehurst, Barbara, *op. cit.*
244 Hunt, Garry, 'The Riddle of Titan's gas', *New Scientist*, 64
     (922), pp 429ff (1974)
245 *Sky and Telescope*, 52, p 419, (1976)

Index

SUBJECTS

NAMES